Ancient Lights

London
Black Sandal
2011

First publised in 2011
by Black Sandal
41 Oriel Road
London E9 5SG
www.blacksandal.co.uk

ISBN 978 0 9564360 16

contents

Alison Marr

Mungo's House

Mungo could hear her tuneless whistling as far away as the kitchen. She'd woken him up by dragging furniture past his bedroom door. He didn't know how long he could stand this onslaught on his nerves. He filled the kettle, and while he waited for it to boil, looked down at his hands; they seemed even hairier now, like mittens. His nose was sprouting too; it must be the male menopause they were all talking about. The shrill notes grew louder as he crossed the hall. From the drawing room door he saw his cousin Penelope, on the stepladder, ruining his cobwebs with her duster. He sneaked up below her and roared, 'Stop that maddening whistling.'

She wobbled, and dragging his curtains with her, crashed on the floor, between the desk and the sofa. Her head lay at an intriguing angle and, compelled to capture it, he grabbed a pencil and paper, and began to sketch but she kept moving and groaning, so he knelt down and bawled in her ear, 'Get up and stop malingering.'

The doorbell went and he could see, by peering down the hall, the doughty features of Mrs Brigid McMalady pressed against the glass. He decided to ignore her but she kept on ringing, and then began to kick the door. He opened it, asking, 'What can I do for you Brigid?'

She dropped her basket saying, 'I've brought you a lobster for I heard you had your cousin over.' He gaped at her and she added 'It's a present.'

'But it's alive,' he said.

'Yes, do you want it or not?' Its nippers clacked

'But what shall I do with it?'

'Well, you could put it in cold water and boil it up real slow and hope it falls asleep or you could buck it into boiling water and instant death. I prefer the second method because you can't hear it scream.

'It screams?' he asked.

'Like a banshee on her period – what's that noise?'

'Oh it's only Penelope – making a fuss.'

Mrs McMalady pushed past him and into the drawing room where Penelope lay among the curtains sobbing. 'In the name of God, are you all right?' she asked her.

Mungo scowled at them and left the house, avoiding the waving lobster in its basket, and walked down the cobbled path to the shore. He carried his sketch pad and box of watercolours. It was a cold, April day and the tide was rushing up the beach. He sat on a rock and looked out to sea. He'd painted this view many times but today felt too jittery to start and decided to go to McMahon's, and, remembering it was Jimmy Mallow's wake, quickened his pace.

McMahon's, the oldest pub in the county, was built in a cave under the cliff. Sea light poured in from slanted, leaded windows. It looked like the captain's cabin in a galleon. It was hung about with nets, green glass globes, driftwood, nautical maps, even a breasted figure head. It was owned by Mary, the last of the McMahons, but she was getting tired and threatened to sell the place.

When Mungo pushed open the door, he saw the mirrors had been draped in black cloth; the coffin rested on a decorating table. Two young men sat around it playing cards on the lid, on which their glasses and ashtrays stood. Mary pulled Mungo a pint of Guinness and set it down with the others, wiping where the liquid had spilled.

'Sit down Mungo and join us in our farewells,' said Bat Sheridan, the local poet. His auburn hair was braided into a long plait and his bare arms wriggled with Celtic knot-work tattoos. Mungo shivered and lowered his big backside to the stove.

'He still owes me thirty euros,' said Gervaise McMalady, 'I wonder what these are worth?' He rattled the handles of the coffin. He was a giant of a man, dark and hairy, with a look of Blackbeard about him.

'They're such a waste – coffins. When I die I want to be left up on the mountain for the eagles,' said Bat.

'Sure, there're no eagles left – the farmers have killed them all, but there're plenty of pigs around here that would happily dispose of you,' said Mary.

Bat frowned into his glass of poteen. It looked benign. He rolled it around his mouth then spat it in the stove where it whooshed out, singeing his boots. It smelled of brimstone and potatoes. He licked his lips and said, 'That's fierce stuff Mary, is it from your man from Antrim? I always feel I can fly when taking it.'

'I never disclose my sources,' she answered.

'And how is Mungo keeping - did she arrive?' asked Gervaise.

'Unfortunately, yes.'

'Why? What's wrong with her?'

'She's an appalling swine. She claims that a new will of Aunt Winifred's says that she has a half share in Henbane

House and she wants to share. Imagine! I'm not giving her an inch. I've lived here for fifteen years. I'm practically fucking Irish. I'd torch it first.'

'I saw a woman going up your path yesterday and she wasn't bad looking,' said Bat.

'Did she have horns?'

'No...she was quite tasty, in a subdued kind of way. Ah, here're the old biddies,' said Bat.

'Don't you refer to my mother and my aunt like that – you little shite,' said Gervaise.

'You got here quick, Mungo. It was terrible of you leaving that poor girl lying on the floor. She was in an awful state. She needs tender loving care,' said Brigid McMalady.

'She needs to fuck off back to London,' said Mungo.

'That's no way to speak of your relations,' Brigid said and shoved him away from the stove with her hip and planted herself in front of it.

'Och, he's not screwed down is he? – I wanted to see him,' said Margaret, Brigid's sister, 'Give us that jemmy Mary. Move boys.'

'You can't do that' Mary said.

'I can so.' With a tearing sound Margaret levered the lid off.

'God, he's an awful funny colour' said Bat.

'He's terracotta,' said Mungo and reached for his paints.

Penelope lay on the damp duvet in the attic. She could hear mice in the walls. Her head and neck ached. Mrs McMalady had been kind but the painkillers and cup of tea had not helped. She was stunned at the ferocity of Mungo's reaction when she told him about the will. He'd screamed and jumped up and down like Rumpelstiltskin and threatened to dig up Aunt Winifred and dance on her bones. '*You will never live here. Henbane House is mine'*, he'd roared at her. When she'd requested he smoke in the garden in future, he'd raised his fist to her face and punched the wall behind her. He hated her. He really did.

Mary was going to stop doing wakes – they were worse than weddings, although people always drank more when there was a coffin present. Only two of Jimmie Mallow's relations had turned up but they were Pioneers and only drank lemonade. They were mortified by their richly hued relation and left early. Bat had gone berserk on the poteen and went out to recite his poems to the sea, while Gervaise disappeared with Lizaveta, the Lithuanian barmaid. Mary'd found them at it in the sand dune where she kept the bins. After a feed of drink Brigid and her sister had regaled them with fearsome dirges on banjo and whistle. Mungo had tolerated this for a while, merely groaning, as though he had toothache, but when Brigid failed twice to reach the high C on *Boolavogue*, he screamed once and left.

    None of them had been fit enough to attend the funeral the next day. She had had to nail Jimmy down before she went to bed. The closest they got to the riddle of why his corpse was orange, was the fact that he grew and traded in carrots.

    She was tired of other people drinking. She thought of the tea dances of long ago, in the ballroom of imagination and desire – the pale afternoons in Errol's arms and sighed. She poured herself another whisky.

Bat lay with his face pressed up against the cold window pane beside his bed. He felt toxic, his mouth dry as a gravel path and his head as though a spade were buried in it. He tried to unravel last night's events but it was murky, though he had an image of himself conducting an orchestra on the Coola road.

From the hymn singing wafting up the stairs he knew his mother was listening to mass on the radio and thought it would be a good time to liberate some of her valium and codeine. He slid out of bed letting the weight in his head propel him and crawled on all fours to her room and rattled through her rake of medicines till he found what he wanted. She could start her own chemist shop, he thought. She had medicines for every part of her body, even her shins had a polish. He crammed the tablets into his mouth and chewed.

Bat followed her through the village. He still felt frail from the night of the wake and rested on the big stone outside the chemist and watched her as she got her messages. She was very tall, with an apologetic stoop and her dress drooped on her, but he liked thin women. She went into Casement's Emporium and came out with a green scarf and a penny whistle. She caught his eye and he clicked appreciatively with his tongue. She blushed and hurried away from him.

'Excuse me,' he said, stopping her, 'I'm a friend of Mungo's. I'd just like to say I hope you're not finding it too quiet here after the big city.'

She stared at him, taking in his tattooed arms and chiselled features.

'I was wondering if you would like to walk out with me some time?'

She looked wary and said, 'I won't be staying here much longer.'

'Oh you mustn't let old Mungo scare you off. He's all wind really – it's his artistic temperament.' Bat danced around her, 'Come on in to Jenny's – I'll treat you to afternoon tea.'

She sat opposite him in the window seat of the cafe, sipping scalding tea, nibbling a scone. Bat wolfed through the sandwiches. 'What do you do in London, Penelope?' he asked.

'Did Mungo tell you my name?'

Bat considered the names Mungo had called her. 'He did indeed now – said you were coming to stay a while.'

'I'm on extended leave,' she answered in a clipped voice.

'Are you on the sick then?'

'Stress – I don't want to talk about it.'

'I went to London once – it was horrible – all those millions – like the Tower of Babel – I couldn't wait to get back.

'It's wonderfully diverse and vibrant,' she said piously and dabbed her mouth with a tissue.

'I like to be able to walk from my house into the woods or go on the seashore and not meet a soul.'

'There are many fine parks,' she sighed and closed her eyes.

'Would you not like to go to the wood to see the bluebells, they're out now?'

'No, thank you, perhaps, another time.'

'Tomorrow then?'

'I don't know.'

'You've bought a penny whistle. Can you play it?'

'No, but Brigid McMalady is teaching me rebel tunes – I want to learn so much…folk music is the music of the oppressed and I want to show solidarity.'

'Don't you be saying that to the McMaladys – they wouldn't appreciate it a bit. If you like music you should come to the session on Saturday night in McMahon's.

'I don't think Mungo would like me going to his local pub.'

'Well, I'm inviting you and if Mungo gives you any grief, well – '

Mungo lay on the sofa listening to Bizet's Carmen on the radio. The room was a mess of feathers where he'd plucked the chicken Brigid McMalady had brought him. This time, she had at least the decency to kill her gift first. The lobster she'd brought him had disappeared. She was a powerful woman – the way she'd wrung the chicken's neck was impressive. He wondered if she fancied him, for she was always bringing him presents. She was only a trifle older than he was and she still had a fine figure. A little porcine around the chops but…there was Gervaise to consider. He could tear a man apart with his bare hands and he was very protective of his mother.

The chicken had been free range – he could tell by the leg muscles. He'd given the gravy a full glass of Bordeaux and now regretted it for he'd finished the bottle and he was still horribly sober. He took his last bottle of wine from his Wellington boot and kissed it farewell. As he dug the corkscrew in, it broke off, so he tried gouging the cork out with a knife but that didn't work. He put the cork in his mouth and tried to pull it out using his teeth, but pulled his dentures out instead. He then placed it in the door jam and yanked and jerked it but it wouldn't budge. He considered going next door and borrowing Betty's opener but she'd want a glass. In despair he looked around the room saw a tin whistle resting on top of Penelope's book. He picked it up and read the title: *A Lexicon for the New World Order*. He shuddered and dropped it and carried the whistle to the fireplace. He took his heavy poker, positioned the mouthpiece of the whistle on top of the cork and whacked it hard. The cork sunk in and wine splashed up.

'What are you doing with my whistle?' Penelope asked.

Mungo spun around. 'Oh it's *your* infernal pipe – whistling with your lips is not irritating enough – you want to drive me completely mad with this.' He pulled it out of the bottle where it dripped among the feathers and flung it at her.

She ducked and cried, 'A little civility costs nothing Mungo,' fleeing from the room.

Mungo ran after her shouting, 'And don't come back.'

At least she'd stopped her incessant cleaning since her fall. He couldn't fathom it. Why, when the wing-backed chair had stood in the hall since Aunt Winifred was a child, minding its own business and not harming a soul, should she want to move it? She had only been here two weeks but the damage she'd done; opening windows, brushing and cleaning and…generally being a pest. He would just leave the feathers. He'd been aghast when Bat had taken a shine to her. 'But she's a great breast-less drip of a woman,' he'd said

19

and Bat answered, 'She's mysterious – she has depths I want to swim in'. It was a pity Bat still lived at home with his mother, although she was dying he remembered, and cheered up.

Penelope dressed carefully and even put on a little scent. She held up her small mirror and tried to see how she looked. Bat was taking her to see the bluebells. She felt excited; he was so young and strange and handsome. But she was fearful too. She'd never been breached. No man had ever taken liberties with her. She would try it – before it was too late.

Mungo was out, so she took out the whistle and tried the tune Brigid had taught her *The Wind that Shakes the Barley* it was called. She played hesitantly but was pleased at the authentic, plaintive quality the notes had. She liked Coola village, its isolation – its long shore – its quiet woods with rooks.

Bat was bursting with urgent juices. He groaned among the bluebells. Penelope had let him have a little play on her bosoms but as soon as he lifted up her dress she'd fled the wood. He was furious. Could she not see the clean beauty of his jaw bone and his Grecian nose? And feel the hot wildness of him, his arms shimmering like the Book of Kells? He lay down and rubbed himself on the drenched blue flowers.

Penelope, scrubbing the bath of fifteen years of Mungo's dirt circles was forced to use planet-harming bleach. The lemons she'd bought had not touched the impervious rings. She desperately needed a bath but could not bring herself to

descend into the mire. She scrubbed harder. A thin wind
blew the cobwebs and stirred the mushrooms on the wall. A
paring of soap the size of her fingernail and a stiff towel
were the only signs that Mungo ever cleaned himself. Beside
the caked toilet was a book *The Hundred and Twenty Days of
Sodom* its pages stuck together. She left the bleach to soak
and explored the room at the end of the passage.

The window was covered in an old sheet. She
pressed the round Bakelite switch. It was Mungo's studio.
His paintings leaned up against the walls in rows. Why did he
have to paint the sea like a sewer, with hydra headed whales,
frowning dolphins and crazy boats made of supermarket
trolleys? And his nudes… lovely girls disfigured with an-
thrax, ringworm on their breasts, leprosy on their cheeks.

Mary liked the afternoons best, the sea light flooded in. She
had always loved her cave life. It had felt safe but now the
drinks were maddening her. Temperance was easy when she
was young but now, menopausal and unbalanced, she felt
like suckling the optics. They smouldered below her as she
slept and called her to their forgetful depths.

Penelope tiptoed down the stairs. She'd been woken by what
sounded like an obscene telephone call coming from
Mungo's room, but it was only him, snoring in stupor. He
was ensconced in Aunt Winifred's French bed. His fat face
spilled onto the pillow and rose and fell like a tide. She
looked at his black devil's eyebrows and remembered the
first time she'd met him, at their grandparent's house in the
North of Ireland – the old manse by the river. She must
have been eight years old and he at least fifteen when he

hunted her down to the hen house, his big, red laughing face filling the doorway, as he told her, 'Your mother doesn't wear any knickers. She's got a big hairy arse. And here's my painting of it.' He was talented even then. It was a horrid picture.

Why had she felt this arrangement could ever work? She thought that his early fame as an artist would have mellowed him – the house was large enough – he might have been glad to share with her. 'His creative juices are all dried up – he's a bitter man', Bat had told her. She'd have to leave – she'd have to go back to all that. She'd go next week. She'd promised Bat she'd go with him to the session. She shouldn't have left him but his ornate flesh had disturbed her.

Mary lit the candles in their sconces along the walls and the little nightlights in their glass containers. Margaret McMalady was tuning her banjo by the stove. Brigid hadn't arrived yet. It was still light outside and the tide on the turn. The musicians usually arrived by nine. There was always a lock-in at the sessions. Even the Guards came. She'd put on her new blue dress with the lace and sent Lizaveta to clear the end of the room for the dancing and went outside to smoke. She sat on the bench by the door and watched the gulls and cormorants fighting over the bread brought for them daily by the Lears – the village idiots. They were brothers and wore matching outfits of black and yellow tartan trousers, pinstriped waistcoats and red berets. Everyone agreed they looked like gentlemen foxes. They were famous for raiding picnics and stealing buns. On nights of the full moon they'd lie on the damp sands and soak up the lunatic rays. Everyone loved them – even Mungo tolerated them.

A swan waddled up the beach, spavined and clumsy,

then back-flapped as it recognised Mungo. He growled in response to Mary's greeting, stomped past her and sat down. His bag clinked as he lowered it. When Lizaveta brought his drink he sat with his hairy arms around it and blew his cigarette smoke in the direction of the door. She didn't know why he came to the session when he so obviously hated the music. He used to turn the television on at top volume as the musicians began to play, but had been persuaded out of that by the bodhran player from Coola. Now, he was reduced to holding his hands over his ears in a blatant way and he always left early. He'd been the hardest to shift outside to smoke, when the ban came in. To enact their intolerable law the government had their spies everywhere, but in the lock-ins she let them smoke, for she knew everyone, even Guard Michael lit up with the best of them. She had not reckoned on Penelope Worthy.

Bat ran into the kitchen of Henbane House and shouted up the stairs 'It's all right. He's just left the off licence and he's away around the shore. Are you ready yet?'

'I'm coming,' Penelope answered.

Bat avoided Mungo's greasy armchair and sat on the sawn-off church pew that stretched against the wall. He idly picked up one of Penelope's sociology books and attempted to read it but, unsure if it was written in English or not, put it down. His amazing arms and chest were covered in a green silk shirt and his auburn hair, released from its plait, tumbled down his back in ringlets. He looked like a Romantic poet, he thought, kissing his reflection in the mirror. There was an evil smell from the range. He opened the door and found a dead lobster inside and shut it quickly.

Penelope pinched her cheeks. She didn't approve of make-up but she looked so wan in the little mirror.

She declined Bat's arm as they left the cottage and marched across the sands ahead of him, carrying her tin whistle like a spear and avoiding the seaweed. She did not want to damage her ethical shoes; the leather from cows that'd donated their hides willingly; or stain her long dress, made of Fair Trade Indian hemp, the colour of sewage. She'd let her hair fall loosely around her and taken off her glasses. The sedative the doctor had given her for her flight she'd put in her purse. She might need it later.

'Are you sure you want to play tonight?' Bat asked her, 'You're just a beginner.'

'I can nearly play a rebel tune and a lament,' she answered.

'Well, if you are sure, and listen, no lectures. Just relax. Mungo leaves early, for he hates the music. We can sit at the bar away from him.'

It was the first break Mary had got. The cave was jumping with the music and the dancers. She went outside. The moon was up and she could see the idiots gambolling near the sea's edge. Mungo followed her, 'Did you see that infernal swine sucking up to Bat? She should have been drowned in a bucket at birth,' he said, swaying wildly.

'I heard her telling Bat she's thinking of going back to London soon,' said Mary, 'I feel sorry for her — she seems uncomfortable in her skin.'

'Like a snake! Saint Patrick – come back,' he shouted, 'your work is not yet done!'

Mungo was happy. He lay warm and contented under his festering bedclothes, the teat of a baby's bottle deep in his mouth. It was full of wine. As he had broken every cup and glass in the house throwing them at Penelope the only vessel remaining was Mrs Malady's grandchild's bottle. It had been left behind on the one occasion she had brought the baby to visit. He remembered – the horror – how she had asked him to hold the mewling milky thing. He could still feel its creepy little fingers grabbing his hair. Although drunk from the pub he had wanted more and tried to open a bottle of wine by his usual method of sticking the bottle in the door jam and pulling but he had jerked rather too hard and the top of the bottle shattered in his hands. He had to sieve the wine, to remove any lingering shards of glass, using a tea strainer into the bottle but as he sucked he commended himself on his inspired choice

He giggled to himself remembering the look on Penelope's face when he had innocently gone over the sand dunes for a slash. How was he to know that the frigid bitch was at that moment attempting to ride his best friend? He was entirely blameless; he had not expected to find lovers in the dunes on such a windy night, especially not that harridan with Bat Boy Sheridan. He could still hear her cry of disgust as the wind caught his water and sent it flying over the two of them. They were all lit up by the moonlight among the scudding clouds – poor damp things. He tried to remember the last time he had tried the fleshly dance but it was so long ago – his landlady in Dublin had taken a shine to him; she suspected money in his round vowels and jumped him one night when he came swinging up the stairs in the old house in Inchicore. He'd let her have her way with him, oh but she was the quare big lump of a woman – breasts on her like bolsters and a great yawning mouth. He could barely walk for a week.

As she lay in the dunes with Bat's lively arms entwining hers, Penelope felt relaxed for the first time since that awful business in Islington. At Bat's insistent kisses she lowered her rigid knees. The valium she had mixed with valerian tea rushed through her veins and she allowed herself a little peck on Bat's fantastic jaw line. That encouraging response thrilled Bat so that he ripped open her long hempen dress and exposed her virginal breasts to the moon. Responding, Penelope slid into Bat's Celtic arms, and mounting him, rode him like she used to ride her rocking horse. She had thrown her ethical shoes to the winds and swooned with joy. Until, that brute Mungo had come, staggering over the marram grasses on his way home, and watered them as they lay in their love basin in the dunes.

Mary had been busy all night. It was not till near closing time that she saw Errol sitting on one of the desiccated deckchairs from the liner *The Lusitania* that had washed up almost a century ago. He sat straight backed and stared at her. She'd dropped a pint of stout causing a momentary silence as the punters looked on with dismay as the black gold dribbled down the sloping floor of the cave. The pub was tiled like a wet room. She went into her room at the back and shut the door. Taking her hand mirror she squinted at her face in its old green glass. She was pale from her days in the cave as she usually only ventured out at dusk when the colours were diffused. Her hair was not yet grey but her eyes, which Errol had once described as being as green as fresh nettles, now looked as murky as a tank full of dying fish. Her smile, a bitter rictus, showed yellow teeth. She sighed, cursing the effect the inexorable march of time had had on her. How could Errol ever find in her old bones the woman he had left twenty years ago? She pulled the hatch and peered out. He had changed little since she had last seen him - still strong faced and dark haired – the unfairness of it. She sank into her old armchair in front of the dead grate until she heard her name being called by Lizaveta.

In the bar sat the brothers Lear in their tartan trousers and waistcoats. They were juggling golf balls they had found on the sands. Bat Sheridan was telling the punters about the ancient bog that lurked beneath the golf course, how oddities had emerged; a bog-oak throne complete with bog-oak queen and bog-oak harper had swum up one day frightening the American golfers. These remnants of a royal past now graced Coola Museum. He told them too that the golf club was cursed and how the golf balls would turn bog oak in flight and become golfer-seeking missiles. The Lear brothers merely smiled and tickled each other under the arm chanting:

> Round and round the garden
> Like a teddy bear
> One stroke…Two strokes
> Tickly under there

Mungo had just come in and said in a loud voice, pointing to them, 'They are the result of a consanguineous marriage.'

'That is the most terrible judgemental thing to say,' said Penelope rising up on her hind legs. Beside her Bat blushed.

'How dare you judge families, there are many different types of family and incestuous families are as valid as any other.' She had her penny whistle in her hand and turning to Brigid McMalady asked her to accompany her on the banjo in one of the two tunes she had learnt especially, as she believed them to be tunes of the oppressed. She did not see how Brigid's brows beetled at the suggestion. No one, well not since she had been in Primary Two, had ever oppressed Brigid.

Penelope stood poker-backed, and began to blow. The tune she attempted was, to be fair, not the easiest for a beginner as it soared up to a high and lonely C. But Penelope, thinking of the Battle of Aughurim, was off, her notes falling and rising till she had conjured herself at the battle and she was, of course, on the side of the defeated and oppressed but then how could she tell who was who on that antique battlefield?

She played on, loving the sad plangent notes of the dirge. Somewhere in her head she heard the crack of bone and sinew and saw the romantic spill of blood. Now she saw noble peasant women come to nurse the wounded but no, they were robbing, stealing the medals and even teeth from the scattered dead. She forced that image away as after all it was all King Billy's fault, for 'othering' the enemy. She shut her eyes as she played which was just as well as she did not see the mass exodus of the customers fighting for the door. Her playing was strident, like a parrot having its little yellow feet sawn off without anaesthetic or a goose being plucked alive. She squawked on regardless.

'Enough, I can't stand it. Shut her up now,' shouted

Mary. She was furious – she had seen her Errol flee with the rest of the pub. Only Bat and Mungo remained and they wore ambiguous expressions. Bat tugged at Penelope's arm to alert her while Mungo smirked and lent across the bar to pour himself another beer.

'It's time you all went home,' Mary said. She looked bleak. She piled the chairs on top of the table and began to brush the floor. Penelope woken from her emotive empathy with the past put her whistle in her pocket and taking Bat by the arm strode to the door. Bat nodded to Mungo and attempted to thank Mary, but Penelope hurried him away. The rush of performing for the first time of her life had stimulated her and she bore Bat through the night. She could not wait to fall into his amazingly welcoming and historically accurate arms.

Mary wanted to go upstairs but remembered there was no upstairs to the cave just back and further back…till it reached the lake of mercury, the stalactite pillars and the marble island where the chieftains lay. She went outside to smoke a cigarette. The wind was up and the beach as empty as a beach should be. There was a tide full and pulsing and a dark blue black sky with a coy moon and a wind to die for and give birth to and be unfaithful with. She looked at her fifty year old hands with the raised veins like the trails on a map and her stumpy nails and thought she saw death in her hands. She was furious that Errol who had sat as immobile as an Easter Island head had stirred himself and dis-appeared. The pub had emptied, even the village idiots, whom she had last seen lying on the bar getting their tummies tickled, had fled. She dragged herself to her room in the hewn rock and crawled into bed.

She was fuming. The front door of her pub had been kicked in by strange guards from Dublin. They were terrifying, with helmets with visors like Judge Dredd and long batons. They had demanded to see her CCTV camera in order to prove that she had let the punters smoke in her pub and they refused to believe that she did not have spy cameras focused on her customers. They tore through the pub looking for tell-tale ashtrays with cigarette butts and were triumphant when they discovered a brimming one under the bar. They had formally charged her for allowing tobacco to be smoked on her premises. They had refused to disclose their source but Mary overheard one of them say that the English mot had been right; Mary would have to go to court. It was a serious offence.

Although it was early, Mary stuck her head under the gin optic and sucked a couple of shots. She then went out and lay on the sand listening to the waves and weeping. She tried to hide the tears from Mungo who came loping over the dunes with his boots hanging around his neck.

'Look at the state of my hands,' he cried, 'they are getting worse.' Wiping her eyes she saw that indeed they were even hairier than before. There were a good three inches hanging down from his palms. 'I look like a frigging werewolf – look at my arse, it's like a forest and my chest too.' He started to unbutton his flies.

'No! No, it's OK I believe you – you should see the doctor – it must be hormonal – men get strange too around your age Mungo.'

'I'm going to shave it off right now, well maybe after

a short – what are you doing out here anyway – it's not like you to idle in the sun on a morning?'

'I had only the Dublin guards kicking the door in this dawn – somebody grassed me up for letting us all smoke and I have a feeling it was your cousin Miss Worthy.'

'That …swine – I could swing for her – can you imagine what she'll do to my house if she gets it – it will be all minimalist with pictures of famine porn on the walls and I'll never be able to relax again – I'll pull her fucking head off and stick it up her arse.'

'Calm now Mungo – don't be doing anything rash, revenge is a dish best cold, remember.'

They sat in the sun. Mungo found a stick and drew pictures in the sand; beside the driftwood a long thin figure of a woman on a scaffold, over there by the blue plastic rope, a woman's head above blazing faggots, and near Mary's feet, a woman stretched on a rack.

'Amazing,' said Mary bending down to admire his sand art. She fetched them both a dram and they sat in a com-panionable silence till they heard Brigid singing along the strand.

'It's raining men Hallelujah – it's raining men. God love you, it's you Mungo and you too Mary sunning your-selves this lovely God-given day but yer hitting it a bit early if ye don't mind me saying so,' said Brigid.

'I had a bit of shock this morning – riot police all the way from Dublin kicking me door in – look at the state of it!' They all turned to the door. It was hanging by one hinge and there were great big boot marks all over it.'

'You would think we were terrorists or something not bloody smokers. I remember a time it was sexy to

31

smoke, I loved Players – you know the packet with the sea captain on it – I had the hots for him, I love hairy men,' said Brigid McMalady shuffling her arse over the sand towards Mungo.

Mungo was so concentrated in his sand pictures that he didn't notice till she was right behind him, till she grabbed his shoulders in her strong hands and began to massage them.

Bat didn't understand why Penelope was so incensed. He had thought it was only a little rain that presaged the coming autumn. 'So poor old Mungo was caught short in a shortcut over the dunes, I'm sure he didn't mean it.'

'Of course he knew we were there. He hates me – he's always hated me,' snapped Penelope. She stood up and looked in the dunes for her ethical shoes.

'Come back to my arms me darling Penelope for I am your Odysseus and you have waited your whole life for me,' called Bat from the hollow where he lay.

But she stomped off shoeless and stumbled along the dunes catching her feet among the roots of the pig nut trees, but all the time she had her eyes on the lights of Coola and her birthright, Henbane House.

The house was dark when she reached it but she knew Mungo was only about fifteen minutes ahead of her. She guessed he would either be in bed or lying in wait for her with a possible sabotage.

She peered through the filthy windows but could make out nothing. She tried the front door but it was locked. She went around the side of the house to the back door but it was locked also. There was a ladder leaning against a damson tree. She shinned up it till she came to her bedroom window. She tried it but the Victorian bolt was on. She found herself close to the silver birch tree and swung into it and climbed higher till she came to Mungo's room. She could see little but then the moon flared behind her and she could see a big hump in the rancid pit that was Mungo's bed. She tapped gently on the window. She saw the hump move. Then a big hairy head raised itself up calling, 'Who's there, who's there?'

'It is Aunt Winifred. I remember how you stole my purse all those years ago in the old house at Derrybane, the house with the wine cellar and the free range servants.' She crooned out the words in the Ulster accent of their aunt.

'Fuck off – you're dead and buried twenty years,' he shouted but his voice, Penelope was pleased to hear, sounded frightened.

'You must leave my house, or share it with Penelope, the poor girl deserves it more than you – you drunken reprobate – you dinosaur, you nasty boy.'

'Go away you old ghost aunt, that vile witch will never get this house, I'd blow it up first. I've got a bottle of holy water here and you'll be getting it in the chops if you don't fuck off back to your grave.' He jumped out of bed and ran across to the table where he grabbed a small bottle, ran to the window and flung it out. He leant over and saw the long thin figure of Penelope scurrying down the ladder.

'Oh it is you.' For once he was speechless, then he stirred himself and ran down the hall and into the bedroom he had let her stay in. Starting with her sociology books he rammed them into a suitcase and threw her ethical clothes on top. When he had collected everything he threw the suitcase out the window and noticed with happiness how all her belongings spilled out and her knickers and bras were hooked on the branches of the tree.

Penelope ran past the rowan trees till she came to Coola Castle and stopped to read the plaque. It had been sacked in the seventeenth century, rather improbably, by the nuns of St Biddy's convent. As her breathing calmed she felt cheered that she had at last stood up to Mungo. Why on earth had she ever thought she could live peacefully with him? He was an unreconstructed bigot from the last millenium. She sat down on a bench and began daydreaming how she could get Mungo back for treating her with contempt. If he barricaded the house against her, why, she would live in a caravan in the back garden. There was a cold-water tap in what remained of Aunt Winifred's conservatory – that would be her water supply, and if Mungo sabotaged that, there was always the well – if she boiled off the scum it would be fine. She'd befriend the local gypsies and invite them in for sessions on their human rights. Mungo would hate that. She could have big fires with picturesque pots hanging over them and she would exchange her ethical clothes for long flowered skirts and dangling earrings. She could learn to play flamenco guitar and tell fortunes and people would see her as a wise woman, a bard, a seer and Bat could write epic poems about her and the dear gypsies. And she would live there all the long days.

It was quiet in the village; a soft white moon peeked out from the clouds. She lay down on the summer seat that had been dedicated to St Biddy and closed her eyes.

When she opened them the sun shining in her eyes blinded her and then she heard Mungo say in his poshest voice 'Yes Doctor Zappa, she attacked me last night, a violent psychopath, with delusions of grandeur – as the next of kin I have the right to have her sectioned.'

Penelope sat up and stared at a small man wearing shades and a T-shirt that said *Jesus sucks*. 'It is not as easy now to have someone sectioned as it was in the olden days. It was great then – you could have tiresome members of your family locked away for life. I remember my great Aunt Pixie was locked up for kissing a boy. The asylum turned her mad. I used to go and throw peanuts at her, she loved peanuts. She used to scale the bars to get them.'

'What were you saying Mungo? Remember it is I who works for the social services not you. If any one around here is to be locked up it is you, for you're mad, bad and filthy,' said Penelope rising to her full height and stalking off, limping a little as her bare feet hit the stones of the lane. She passed Bat's house and glanced into the ground floor window but she was met with the angry face of Mother Bat who scowled at her and gave her the sign of the evil eye.

She stopped at the Best Buns Bakery and bought herself two croissants and a coffee and took them back to Henbane House. When she got there she saw the front and back doors padlocked and draped with razor wire.

A mangy old Staffordshire dog with pink boiled looking eyes was chained up in the yard and snapped at her. Her clothes were hanging from the tree making it like it one of the holy trees of spells and devotions that were found in Coola woods. Her books lay scattered around the garden. She sat down on Mungo's swing and wept, then slowly ate both croissants and drank her coffee and began to gather up her belongings into her suitcase.

The night had been damp and her beautifully bound copy of *A Lexicon for the New World Order* was wet and muddy. She found her trainers and put them on and limped along the road to Bat's house and knocked but when his mother opened the door she had a baseball ball bat in her hand and screamed 'Get to fuck away from my door and if I ever see you hanging around my son you'll be spitting teeth out for weeks.' Used to dealing with angry clients in her job she gave her conciliatory smile and backed away.

She walked along the sand dunes picking at the grasses until she came to McMahon's pub, where its sign with the furious mermaid swung in the wind. Leaving her suitcase at the open door she went towards the bar. The pub went silent. 'Could I have a small glass of wine please?' she asked Mary.

'No, we're out of wine,' said Mary and took a long gulp from her own glass.

'A cup of tea then.'

'No, in fact Miss Worthy ye are not welcome here any more. Look at see the state of my front door – that's all your work so it is.'

Penelope glanced at the door and saw that it was detached and leaning against the wall and heard the sea wind as it whipped through the pub shaking the curtains and pictures. 'What do you mean Mary – what is all my work?'

'You sent the guards here to do me for letting my friends smoke and they kicked the door in and now I've been summoned to court and I'll get a big fine. So I hope you're pleased.'

'But Mary I was trying to help you and your customers, you have no right to allow them to harm themselves with cigarettes. They need to have their awareness raised about the danger of smoking and passive smoking too. On this matter the state knows best.'

'We are grown adults Miss Worthy and it is none of your business to lecture and patronise us. I suggest you leave.'

'I'm looking for Bat.'

'Well, he is not here, he ran off when he found out what a traitor you are. We gave you friendship and that's how you rewarded us – you're not wanted here no more, so goodbye.'

Penelope felt tears spit in her eyes and stifled a sob. She heard a chuckle and looked up to see the hairy triumphant face of Mungo leering at her. He came closer, took a cigarette, lit it and blew smoke right into her face. The customers went back to the serious business of drinking and Penelope left the pub and walked along the shore till she came to the large stone which marked the bus stop. She munched on samphire she'd picked from the edge of the sea.

When Bat crept up the back entry to his house he was relieved to see his mother up a ladder washing the grease from the wall above the range where she cooked. 'So you're not dying anymore Mammy – that's grand. Away and make me one of your lovely beef stews for I haven't eaten properly the whole time you were supposed to be dying.'

'I woke up this morning feeling a new Mrs Bat and I can feel the sap rising in my marrow. I blame it on the new doctor we have, he changed my medication. He said I was suffering from an old idiosyncrasy and it's gone now.'

Bat went up to his room, got out his paper and pen

and began to compose a villanelle, pausing occasionally to blow kisses at his reflection and pout into the wardrobe mirror.

Mungo had barely got into the house, throwing a dead rat he found on the beach at the Staffordshire to relax him, when a knock came on his door. It was Mrs McMalady. She had a bottle of single malt whiskey and a cooked chicken in her arms.

'I thought you would like to celebrate getting rid of that young busybody cousin of yours. I never thought that she would turn on us like that after the way we welcomed her into the village, well maybe not you Mungo but I was always pleasant to her. Anyway, I want to talk straight to you. You must have noticed that since my husband Gerry passed away I've been an awful lonely woman but I'm still in my prime. Look at me bust.'

Mungo looked in horror as she took off her coat and thrust her impressive bosom towards him. He was so shaken at the thought of her confined flesh spilling all over him that he put the whiskey bottle to his head and took a long draught.

'And I have my womanly needs and I know you feel the same about me. I've seen you looking at me when you think I'm not looking and I can see the desire in your eyes.'

Despite the whiskey warming him he began to inch away from her saying, 'Indeed Brigid you're a fine looking woman but you see,' he faltered and thought wildly of an escape route. 'Thing is Brigid, I'm not a well man, look at my hands.' And he stared at his paws in awe, remembering how Bat had taken the strimmer to them only yesterday and how they were now, including the palms, covered in a coarse fringe of red gold hairs.

'They're gorgeous so they are – I like a hirsute man,' said Brigid.

'That's what I've got, a hair suit, I'm completely covered, there is not a bit of skin left, I don't know what to do, but all I can say Brigid, you'll have to give me some time.' And he rushed her to the door, pushed her outside and took himself, her bottle of whiskey and her warm chicken over to the stove where he opened the door and put his feet into the oven. There was a horrible burning smell, but he didn't care and after a good chew at the breast and another long drink he fell asleep.

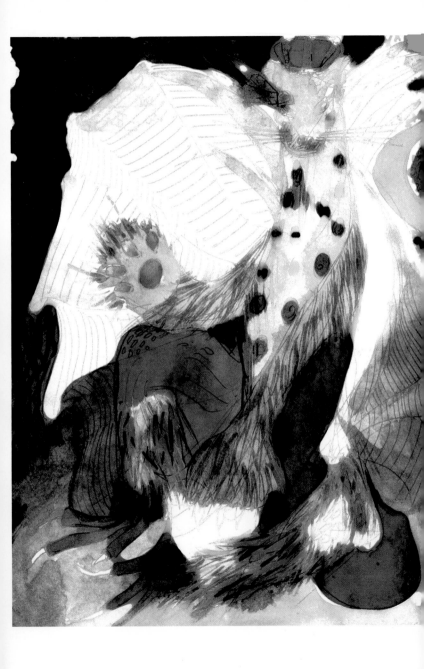

Peace Envoy

After his moral prestige flaked off
we could all see his scales
his inner reptile was released and
his cold mercenary eyes were everywhere
the TV blared with him – the world-wide-web
reeked with him – compassion was resting in
his account making riches for his sharp wife to
swallow up with her great child bearing mouth
he had found God who had blown
bubbles of righteousness for them to travel in
so they bowl along in their bright bubbles
to the Bohemian Grove to sacrifice care to
the Owl God who probes the redwood forests
with its round remorseless eyes

Nevermore O Tahiti   by Gauguin

She has summoned the Devil Bird and it paces the sill
watching the night sky swell like a dark rolling sea.
She is an ecstasy of warm flesh on the sombre bed
where the blue flowers pulse like wounds
Her body sighs and her eyes spit with fierce lights –
she is impatient to go. In the closet her feathers rustle.
She wants to fly with the Devil Bird up into the night
till they stand at the door of the moon,
tapping tap tapping at the door of the moon

Rain on the Pram

I ran through strings of white rain
that drummed on the navy hood
shook the strung ducks of your pram.
Under your bonnet your fat baby face burst
with joy and I wanted to shrink down
to join you in the snug world of infant

Every Day

Mother at the sewing machine, pins in her mouth,
around her bales of satin, gingham, seersucker.
Now she's carrying a shovel of fire to my sick-room grate
bringing me chocolate and the *Bunty*.
At black dawn she'd chop wood in rat yard
boots under her nightdress, old army coat buttoned high,
hands raw with chilblains she'd make the fire.
She had magic – could make anything, a poem or a cake
or a velvet cloak for posing in – she'd paint her dreams,
dipping her brush in her wine, whistling tunelessly,
all lit up and her eyes the blue of Delft.
On baking days she'd roll pastry, chop tart apples,
Christmas she'd pour whiskey into fruit cakes,
make our dolls crinoline dresses, feed the bright robins.
At Halloween when the moon bobbed orange
she'd hide silver sixpences in our pies,
shiver us with ghost stories,
find princes and fortunes in our tea leaves,
every day and every day.

The Whiskey Bottle

It was my uncle's job, after the blitz in Belfast, to inspect damaged houses. The Easter attack had been fierce; Belfast, the least defended city in Britain, had taken a hammering. The Luftwaffe had gone for the docks and the factories. Three thousand were killed. People fled the city in droves, a sad snake of humanity, wriggling into the countryside, with prams and carts full of their rescued possessions and children perched on top. There was such a housing shortage that people slept out on the Black Mountain, one of the high hills that circled the city, causing one local politician to complain that it was disgusting that Protestant and Catholic families had to huddle *together* on wet hillsides.

He told me about the night he came to drink the whiskey; a night full of moonlight and crunching glass. He'd come to the last house in the street with his workmate. It was getting dark. He said it was scary going into the damaged houses – some had great cracks that ran the length of them, as though their spines were broken. He marvelled at how the possessions, blasted apart, settled again in odd juxtapositions. The last house seemed strangely untouched and they stretched out their legs on the sofa in the parlour. They were exhausted; both their houses had been damaged and they, like so many of their neighbours were sleeping anywhere they could find, in their case, in the church hall.

My uncle looked up and saw a bottle of whiskey

winking at him from the top of the dresser. He says it sang to him as well, so he hopped up and got it down, saying to his mate, 'Sure, we're worn out with all the hard work. Sure aren't our nerves ruined with the grief the auld Germans are dishing out? We deserve a wee drink after all that.' They fetched two glasses, pulled out the cork and got stuck in, and soon the fear and pain and all the nervous tension were gone. It wasn't long till they began to sing *After the ball was over* and they'd just started on the *White Cliffs of Dover* when an apparition of an old lady in dusty black appeared before them.

They were terrified till she spoke, saying, 'In the name of God tell me that you're not drinking that whiskey that was on the dresser?'

My uncle jumped up and said, 'I'm sorry Missis; sure we'll buy you another bottle. Weere nerves were bad, after all that banging and destroying, sure we thought the house was empty and everyone fled...'

The old woman interrupted, 'That is the whiskey I use to wash my husband's leg ulcers with. It cleans out the pus lovely. I pour it back in the bottle afterwards. Please tell me the pair of yous hasn't been drinking it. You'll be poisoned if you have.'

My uncle never ever touched whiskey again.

The Pig's Head

It was the first day of the school holidays but it was very dreary. The sky hung low and grey and hot over the village and the sea. I'd spent all day playing with my cousin Penny on the rocky beach in front of my house. We had round plastic water bottles, like cowboys had, tied to our belts and in our rucksacks Abernethy biscuits, apples and chocolate. We were looking for adventure, Red Indians to fight and we slapped ourselves on the hips and galloped along, being both the horse and the rider.

Our mothers had sent us out to play as they were busy making curtains for the gentry in the castle. We had never seen such beautiful material before and kept stroking it but they shouted at us to go away. It was brocade, a very pale rose with fine gold threads worked into strange and beautiful flowers. Our mothers worked in one of the abandoned slum houses in the back street. They had their sewing machines there and their tailors' dummies. They were always tired, with pins in their mouths and cigarettes burning away in clam shells. After their day's work they had to go home and feed their hoards – my mother's hoard had four other children and a crazy husband. Penny's mother, my aunt Maisie had three children and a solid husband.

As we passed the rotting barge which was almost hidden by slimy seaweed, we saw a courting couple leaning up against it. I felt sorry for the poor girl when I saw his big mitt sliding up her white blouse. They were standing with their feet sunk up to their ankles in black mud. They must have been drunk. We cantered right around the bay and away from the village till we came to a grassy mound between the last field and the sea and started our fire. We kept our drift-wood here under the hedge where the heronry was. We collected driftwood, the best pieces I saved for my mother, for she loved them for their pale smooth wood; she kept them in our front garden, some looked like snakes and alligators and she used to grow small plants out of them and pour yogurt over them to encourage moss and lichen. She even had a white crucifix planted, but Daddy told her to take it down as it might encourage passing martyrs. We were twelve and we didn't want to grow up and take our horrible periods. We used to get laughed at by the other kids who smoked and did sex up in the lanes.

Our fire took a while to light as the air was so still but we lay down and blew into the wigwam of little dry sticks till it caught. It was a fine fire and gave off green and blue flames and smelled of sparkly salt. Penny had stolen sausages from Aunt Maisie's pantry and we rammed them on sticks and stuck them into the flames. They crackled and turned black but when we bit into them the insides were still pink and wet, but we ate them anyway. It was very hot and close and the sky looked like dirty brass.

'There's going to be a storm,' Penny said and she ran into the sea in her gutties. We always wore shoes while paddling because the shore was full of sharp shells and stones and nipping crabs. When the tide was out the bay was black and bristled with bedsteads and shopping trolleys, bicycles and the bones of drowned kittens and cats.

I followed her in and we stood there with our skirts

held up and the water nearly touching our navy blue school knickers. The water was cool and exciting and I wished I'd brought my costume.

'We could go in in the nude,' Penny said.

'No, there are too many boats around – imagine, it would be all around the town before we could get home.'

It was true. You could not fart in our town and get away with it.

On the way home Felix Taylor was wading ashore from his red boat with a great basket of mackerel.

'Give these to yer ma's,' he said and handed us about twelve silvery fish, strung on a hoop through their mouths. We were always being given fish and our mothers hated it as they were the ones that had to gut them.

When I got home my mother was running around trying to tidy up the house, tossing our toys and books into our bedrooms and then running in and picking up our discarded clothes scattered on the floor.

When she saw the fish she sighed and said, 'Don't tell yer Da, for I'm not cleaning those and boiling the head.'

I wondered what she meant and laughed as I imagined her boiling our headmaster for he was a horrible bald man with a cane and a Bob Dylan whine.

It was Friday night, the best night of the week; my brother John's folk band would come and play and it always turned into a party and sometimes even a fight.

I helped Ma by peeling the potatoes but I wouldn't cut the onion because onions have always terrified me. I don't know why; something about them having so many skins to hurt. When Mammy served my portion she would pick all the onions out of my bowl. She was very kind; when we had to take medicine she would scoop out the raspberry centres in Raspberry Ruffles and fill them full of pink medicine and then wrap up the sweets again in their lovely red papers. My Granny said she was mad and what we needed was a good skelp around the legs. I watched as Mammy lifted a large bag out of the cupboard and pulled out a pig's head. It sat on the draining board looking a bit like John the Baptist, very sad with a tufty head. She filled the tin bucket she boiled the towels in and placed the head in it and put it on the electric cooker.

I went up the back garden to pull carrots, parsley and celery from our vegetable patch for the stew. When I was there my collie Brandy came up and licked my hand. He was chained up in disgrace for biting the paper boy on his nipple. I told Brandy I'd help him escape later and take him for a roll in the mud at the edge of the bay.

When I came down again the pot was boiling and there was scum raising up like lava which me Ma kept spooning off and sighing. 'Can you smell that Christine? It's horrible,' she said and turned the pan to low, then moved to the sink and began to wash up the breakfast dishes which were all dried and hard. She left them to soak and went out to sit on the shore wall. She lit a cigarette and sucked hard.

'There's John now,' she said and we watched him coming along in his green grammar school uniform. He always had a superior air to the rest of us who went to the secondary modern school with the black and yellow outfit that made us look like convicts and wasps. He was nearly eighteen and studying hard for his A levels. He was the golden boy in our family and could do everything well. He played the fiddle and the guitar and sang like John Lennon.

He could paint landscapes and portraits too. We should have hated him but he was so decent we all loved him. He was tall and slim and golden haired, like a young lord, with an aristocratic face; in fact we all had aristocratic faces, Granny said we had the Habsburg chin.

When he saw us he ran over and kissed Ma on her cheek and tickled me under my royal chin.

The party was in full swing when we heard Daddy coming in. His voice rang out even over the sound of a squeezebox, a whistle, guitar and fiddle. He was a big show-off and liked to make an entrance. He was singing one of the Neapolitan love songs he had learned in Italy during the war but this one had dirty words. Mum and Granny and Auntie Maisie looked at each other and rolled their eyes. Penny and I got new straws for our Coca Cola bottles and then went up the back garden to give Brandy some of the meat left over from the stew. I asked him if he wanted to go for a roll in the mud but he didn't answer, just lay with his lean head on his paws and yawned showing his black serrated mouth and I thought I'd let him rest.

When we came down again I saw Daddy had a bottle of *Sandeman's* port on his lap and he sang along with John and his friends, Damon and Sean accompanied them. Granny played a mean penny whistle and Penny and I banged a tin drum. Daddy had a sweet voice when he wasn't ranting and he sang a love song *Peggy Gordon*. Daddy was torn – he was a Dubliner who loved Irish traditional music but he was also a Protestant who claimed to have been persecuted as a minority in a Papist theocracy. He hated all rebel and nationalist songs. Our John complained that he was denied his Irish culture in the North because he was a

Protestant and Daddy was furious that Irish culture had been rammed down his throat whether he wanted it or not while in the South. Mammy said they were both schizoid and begged John not to sing anything that would set him off, for when roused he was a buck eedjit and would send everything flying – once he threw the baby over the shore wall but luckily the tide was in and wee Danny only got a dip.

Mammy brought in the poor pig's head on the silver platter and set it down in front of Daddy. Although it still looked like John the Baptist it now appeared really furious and red. Daddy gave a roar of joy and took the platter and started to blow on the steaming head to cool it down. We all looked at each other in disgust. Daddy had a thing about offal, he adored tripe, liver and tongue, trotters and ears and he especially loved eating the sexual organs of animals, the sweetbreads. Poor Mammy had to prepare all the offal and she told us she was so sickened she wanted to become a vegetarian.

Daddy had started to lick the face when John started to play mournful chords and sing a rebel song:

In Mountjoy jail one Monday morning
High above the gallows tree
Kevin Barry gave his young life
For the prize of liberty
Shoot me like an Irish soldier
Do not hang me like a dog
For I fought to save old Ireland
On a cold September morn.

There was a chill in the air. Daddy stopped chewing the cheeks of the pig and held it away from him at eye level. Grease shone on his face. John and his friends sang away unaware of the changing atmosphere. Then with a roar Daddy flung the pig's head across the room where it hit John on the head with a biff sound and slid down smearing grease over his white shirt, slithering over the guitar and landing on the floor.

There was silence. We all looked at John who sat with his mouth wide open and his two musician friends who politely looked down at the pig with its gnawed cheeks. Then Aunt Maisie, Daddy's sister let out a big scream of laughter and soon we were all laughing, except Daddy, who picked up the pig's head and carried it out into the front garden shouting, 'Treacherous ingrates.'

We watched him through the window. He was sitting on the shore wall his face buried in the pig's face, like a lover, removing it occasionally to greet the locals as they passed him. There was little left by this time, only the eyes remained and glared over at us with an Old Testament wrath.

Jan Skácel

translated from Czech by
Martina Jirankova-Limbrick and Simon Pettifar

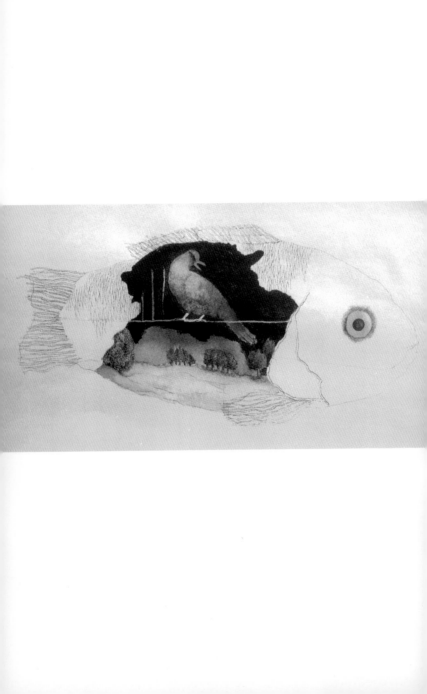

Modlitba za vodu

Prayer for water

Vanishing are the places where once she would go for water
my age-old love
where does would quench their thirst where the tree-frog
                                                    dwelt
and where pilgrims would bend over the water's surface
to drink from their palms

The water remembers
the water is beautiful
my water
the water has let down her hair
protect this water
do not allow the ancient mirror of the stars to go blind

And bring to this water a small horse
bring a horse as black as night
the water is sad
my water
the water has her hair tangled
and who will dive to the very bottom
who will dive to the stars for a little ring

The water is a grieving widow
my water
the water has her hair strewn with ashes
the water is complaining about us

Krátký popis léta

Brief description of summer

Fires From four sides the summer is on fire

The intoxicating scent of acacia groves in bloom
the green soul of the vine smouldering in the vineyards
poppies bleeding among the corn

Darkness is falling
and the moon processes over a silver bridge

The world is like a loaf fresh from the oven
and the night is partaking

Večer

Evening

In the sky wind is gathering,
tomorrow's wind glowing red,
and again love,
again, from of old
from afar stands in the way of death.

Kvetoucí alej

Avenue in bloom

In a white avenue
we held our breath.
Like snow the blossom lay
high up in the trees.

And each tree
proudly celebrated life here
and tirelessly bore
its blossoming strength.

I was breaking words
like rocks in an old quarry.
My wife said only:
I would like to live in this tree.

Co zbylo z anděla

What was left of an angel

In the morning,
as long as all the trees remain swathed
and things untouched,
between two poplar trees an angel floats,
catching aloft his fill of sleep.

Through the chinks in his sleep he sings.

Whoever is first on the street
is likely to be wounded by this singing,
perhaps they sense something,
but they glimpse nothing.

Only greenness
and that is all that is left of the angel.

Přísloví

Proverbs

I was so worried about the state of the world
that I began to invent proverbs.

There are long truths and there are short ones.

And if the punishment does not come immediately,
you must live out your guilt through life.

And no one can undo a deed.

And no one can compose a song
for a little blind girl and a wingless bird.

Smlouva

Agreement

I don't want to be a beneficiary of this or that god.
I've long had my own
for my own needs, my own straightening.
And for humility, which I am in need of.

Sometimes it happens that the human soul stinks
like the coat of a wet dog.
I say nothing against that. Only I want pain
to be truly painful and a tear to be a tear.

Vteřina v lednu

A second in January

And the day is quiet, as fragile as an eggshell.
Inside the sun, also all white.
Even the snow is white, the trees, roofs, snow.
Even this second, even this white moment.

Kdo nás napomene

Who will admonish us

One day the ash will tell us
what door it is they're knocking on
with such stubborn anguish,
the human hearts of this world.

And perhaps love will tell us
why the heart never ceases
and why it always, always
beats at this great door.

But who will reveal
(to my scepticism)
where this door leads
and what is hidden beyond it.

And who will admonish us
without hurt
and yet sternly,
YOU ASK IN VAIN.

And who will admonish us.

Smutky

Sorrows

There are three great sorrows in this world
Three sorrows so great and no one knows
How to avoid these great sorrows

The first sorrow   I do not know where I will die
The second sorrow   I do not know when it will happen
And the last   I do not know in which part of the
                                  beyond I will find myself

Thus I heard it said in a song   Let's leave it at that
Let's accept how the song goes   Let's find it in our power
To take hold of anxiety as if it were the handle of a door
                                                                          and enter

Pravidlo pánských jezdců

The rule of the lords' riders

A pungent whiff of horses like bushes of
blackcurrant and a water ditch
approaching fast
And the riders who feel at their heels
the thought of death
mentally repeat to themselves the old rule

First of all one must toss one's heart over the obstacle

Many will do so
And once they have sailed over the ditch in an arc
they will have no time for looking back
Time backward is the forbidden direction

Meanwhile blood flies up the cherry trees and slaughter
flutters like a banner
The contest is at its end even the summer is over
autumn comes in peaceful again somewhat darker

And the riders who overcame the obstacle
are returning on foot to the place
where once in advance they ditched their hearts
and with bowed head they search in the grass

Perhaps they will find them   And perhaps they will not

Endre Ady

translated from Hungarian by Erzsébet Csicsery-Rónay

A Krisztusok mártírja

The Martyr of the Christs

The banks of the river Ér
Filled me with a passion grand and wild,
My soul was purely pagan,
Full of blind hope and careless desire.
The world turned round me,
Noisy, confused, and barbarian,
And I searched more and more
For some grand Harmony.

I was born a peasant Apollo
Who sang, was strong and pagan
Who, while making love and singing,
Falls at the twilight of life.
Now no more is my soul
Seething with pagan strength, song, and desire
They've killed it, the evangelists,
The philosophers of life and the christs.

A Halál lovai

The Horses of Death

On a white road lit by moonlight
When the shepherds in the sky
Herd their cloud-flock
Unshod, toward us, toward us
The horses of death trot

Noiseless, murderous chargers
Shadow knights on their backs ride
Woeful, wordless shadow knights
The Moon herself recoils in fear and hides
When they go down that white road

Where they come from nobody knows
The whole world sleeps
They loosen their stirrups, they stop
There is always a free steed
And a saddle to ride

And he before whom they stop
Grows pale and mounts the steed
And galloping with him down that white
Road in the bright moonlight
Death searches for new travellers in the night

A Sátán kevélye

Satan's Arrogant One

Let him live his life to the end in disdain
Satan's anointed arrogant one

Faded, his petals should not fall
He was a red flower: he should be blood-red

His mouth may twist in complaint
But he should kick whoever pities him

He should pretend to reject
A jilted lover

And should he kneel as he prays
He should jump up if others see him

Should he believe and wait, hope and fear
He should cry that he is an unbeliever

Should doubts knife his heart
He should sing the praises of the Lord

He should never be a fool for a woman
And should he live and die for her, never say so

Should instinct drive him into a fugitive kiss

He should faint a hundred times and swear

If want and illness ravage
He should come and go as if he were making merry

Should Death caress his bones
He should play the Carnival fool

He should court his enemies
As if he hadn't a care in the world

Christ should not guide him, not even as a joke
Who loves him, he should not love in return

And if Life should tear him to pieces
Death came, because he wanted it

(Satan's arrogant one, the unlucky one
Oh, I didn't live like this, I didn't live like this.)

Finita

It's over. The curtain has fallen
It was a bad play. It flopped.
So you performed better than me…?
…You had a better part.
I played a crazy poet
Who catches fire, hopes and loves
You tricked the poet.
Can there be a better part…?

Too bad the audience was sparse,
It didn't get the deserved applause,
Though for such an excellent part
At other times, you got a lot.
Not for the first time, this role
Was a big success.
There were other crazy poets
Who dared believe in themselves…

Myself I will never blame
For this ignominious flop.
This was the final disappointment
The last rapture of the heart,
For the last time, I burst into flame,
It was only a dream, a silly, fitful light;

It was broken in a cruel game
It went out in a girl's heart…

It's over. The curtain has fallen,
The string quivers a last chord.
My faith, my youth, all gone
For the last time, I was a troubadour…
Until now I desired for desire's ardour
Now I have no more faith, not even in faith
I no longer believe in the crazy tale
Of innocence and virgin white

It's over. The curtain has fallen.
It was a bad play. It flopped.
For me, it was perhaps fatal,
You got the applause.
That's how laurels are handed out on earth
Where the fate of the heart is misery
How many such plays have been performed
On this monstrous stage?

Klára Inotai

translated from Hungarian by Maria Schiller and Hilary Kassman

Hogy valami maradjon belőlem ...

That something might remain....

Before known but unendured
forces close the earth over my eyesgg
and my body, once lauded
by many murmuring mouths, is eaten
by pitiless worms and my outstretched arms
in lieu of an ecstatic embrace
receive thudding clumps of earth;
before the light fades forever,
and I am finally forgotten,
with my last strength I send word to you
that something of me might remain . . .

The heart is silent, the brain has crumbled,
but if you wander lost in thought
along a quiet road before dusk,
mist settling on the distant hills,
heart sore for a companion beside whom to rest,
the sun will project onto earth, leaves and stone
an ever growing, more beautiful image of my wretched self,
the green silk of grass preserving my hand's caress,
drops of water the glimmer in my eyes.

Knowledge awakens dread in the heart
and although the brain proudly bears a hundred wise sayings,
it has no magic to fly beyond the circle
of the body's declining substance.
If sitting alone in the lamplight,
wearied by the doctrines of the day,
you are burdened with the harshness of life,
conjure up someone from far in the past,
a stumbling, pathetic ignoramus,
who embraced you long ago, before becoming nothing.
Although no bridge is built between our worlds,
silence prevailing in that domain
perhaps will offer you consolation in your dejection.

Before I step through the wide gate into that other world,
while life barely supports me on half an arm
yet death has still not gained a total hold on me,
as new pain mingles with the old
and I whisper unheard,
grant me one final boon,
nothing, nothing other than your name,
that I can barely utter.
With gasping breath,
my dying self reaches out,
that it may faithfully illumine for you
my dissolving brain's last shining
ray of light.

Karen Campbell

Belt Beating Man

Yuh uncivilised belt beating man
yuh try fi beat mi bodily
yuh try fi beat mi professionally mentally

But yuh did it unsuccessfully
yuh no have no brought up-sy
yuh try fi mash mi credibility
and yuh try fi tun mi pickney gainst mi

Is mad yuh mad or a crazy yuh crazy?
true say de almighty have a plan fi mi
him tek mi tun all arty farty
and nuh mi ah write dis ya poetry

Mi nah go worry bout no peeny wally
try as yuh might yuh na go broke mi
and mi na gwan let yuh use
yuh evil belt fi lash mi

Kevin O'Hagan

You can keep the money

You can keep the money
it's not the thing that hurts
I hurt myself
for trusting you
even though I knew
I should not

I waited for this ending
I knew it would come
It hurt
that I waited
that's
what really hurts

Naomi Foyle

Unlikely Erotic Objects (No. 17)

In a dimly lit office
on a winter afternoon,
their hands suspended
above a low table,
he offers her a paper clip.

As her fingertip and thumb
pinch the bottom lip,
a hair's breadth
from his touch,
she senses a glint in the room —

a slow blink in her awareness
of the slender loop
between them
as they sit and talk
about the thin white sheets

resting on her lap.
Silently slipping
back into the grey
folder of the day
she tries hard not to think

of the paper clip twisted open,
discarded on the floor:
corkscrew, blade and scissors
hot and jabbing
at the air.

Black Wooden Shoes

after Edmund White's Genet

Five boys. One wielding needle and coal dust.
Two squatting on your biceps.
Two sucking your toes. Tongues gliding
over blistered balls, grimy soles,

as you arch your back, claw the earth
and the gleaming rudder of a frigate
chews your chest.
                              Oh they knew
how to tattoo you at Mettray —

you, my spoiled orphan,
Virgin Father, lousy thief.
Poetry is will, you wrote,
not sensuality.

Bardy Griffiths

Tokyo Tofu

On the 8th floor of the 3rd building of the 7th department
store
next to the arts space,
where a 1000 music appreciators
take the 90 second descent
from perfect note to empty landscape,
is the tofu restaurant.

Green jelly tofu
cools the city's heat.
In lost spaces with concrete benches
the skimmed skin of the warmed soya milk
lies like bird droppings
under the tortured trees.
Among the drained bean husks,
men who had dared to let loose an individual fact
are lulled by the cicadas
defined forever like the thin taste of miso soup.

.

Paul Overy

Seal Souls

Seals were thought to be
souls of dead mariners,
once a year to be released
from their flippers to walk
upright on the land again.
Meanwhile, as mermaids
they could sing, sirens
on rocks to lure
men to their deaths,
increasing the number of sleek
sad-eyed souls.

War Baby

Born in the blitz, my mother
dropped me on my head
when a bomb fell on our flats.
Evacuating us to safer soil, my
father took the train to town, put
on his tin helmet, dragging the corpses
from the rubble, dug out survivors,
often finding the dead in their beds
as if peacefully sleeping, their bodies and
faces unmarked, their lungs collapsed.
Meanwhile my mother boiled water in a pail
to wash me in a zinc bath in the kitchen,
talking wistfully of 'before the war',
a never-never land of bananas and
ice-cream I never entered
but dreamed of as the bombers droned;
the privilege of those to whom
rape and pillage, exile and shame,
choice and blame, collaboration
or resistance, never became
contingent, only names
for the experiences of others, distant
distinct.

Hey (one squirrel to another)

Hey, good looking grey, come
over here to play what
you know best. Say
what you have to say,
take us a bit further
down the line. How
is the weather up there?
Pray for us lesser
mortals. Tell that fellow
with the beard we want
to climb in through his
portals. Good heavens!

Hey! Good looking grey, prey
for us lesser mortals.

George Waser

Layers. Thin Tasfer brushed over
one another   energy

energy + then here is academic discipline
precision plotted formulae
take out a section from the landscape +
creating a pattern or motif extraction

Good-bye Boris

For some days past I have been in a state of nervous agitation, and the thought of Boris, or more precisely of his future, has disturbed my night's rest as well. Yet the word future must be understood in a strictly limited sense. In fact, I have decided to put an early end to the life of this parvenu.

True, the act as such does not frighten me in the least, nor will it burden my conscience. The only question is how the public will take a sudden removal of Boris, a point which troubles me all the more since he is relatively well-known. For a time the technical aspects of my plan were the main problem. But after long and painful hours of introspection I feel strengthened in my intention to contrive a spectacular exit for Boris, some manner of death in keeping with his character. Everyone knows how sentimental the masses can be in their judgement, and I certainly would not want to be reproached with a lack of delicacy, far less with brutality. I am very touchy in this respect! Although there can be no doubt that Boris has sinned heavily and risked his reputation, it was I who made him what he is.

Once again the tolling of the hour from the nearby clock-tower has made me start. If only I could be rid of this accursed restlessness! Unsteadily my fingers clasp the worn wooden shaft which I have just lifted and which, as a rule, I manipulate with dexterity. For a moment it seems to me as if the door opposite conceals something. I feel a stab of fear at the thought of those fatal trifles which the man of action tends to overlook in planning his moves. I dare not even think of what a mistake of mine might bring in its wake – now, immediately before the finale.

The room darkens, and turning towards the window I notice that the sun has begun to set behind the clock-tower. As often before I am captivated by the peculiarity of this structure. Above all, the statues of the clock have fascinated me time and again: there are seven of them, one for each day of the week. From on high these sentinels observe the events in the streets and alleys which have become the scene of Boris Romanov's misdeeds. You, my dumb heralds, I now call up as witnesses when I punish him who has recklessly deprived me of my friends' affections …

Everything had started well. When late one evening in the small wine tavern underneath the city gate I mentioned Boris for the first time, there was an enthusiastic conviction among those present that this newcomer would be well received in society. I freely confess, though, that unlike the merry company who were busy drinking to him, I was not entirely ignorant of the worrisome tendencies of Boris's character. It was close on midnight as I made my way home, and I was just in time to catch a glimpse of the silent changing of the guard in the clock-tower overhead. One of the statues had slipped off effortlessly into darkness, while its successor made ready for its appearance. It was Luna who then stepped out to announce the second day of the week. I was filled with misgivings when I saw the goddess of the moon, but eventually I banished my forebodings and thought of the general sympathy that existed for Boris. Soon after, I arrived in good spirits in front of my house. The following morning, however, I had to tell his perplexed well-wishers that my protégé had already seduced a cavalry colonel's wife.

Tension rose within a few months. Abandoning all restraint, Romanov in turn cheated three respected citizens out of their property, and after a duel – with dire consequences for Boris's opponent – the first voices were heard demanding his head. Exasperated by my connections with him, friends and relatives began to desert me; they called me an eccentric, unsociable fellow, and in the end withdrew completely. I realized that something had to be done, but since Boris had long ceased to be an object of local interest only I faced a delicate task. With some trepidation I decided to send him into exile. The morning of my last preparations I was roused by the sudden peal of the monastery bells, which are still rung once a week as a reminder of the Turkish onslaughts in the days of yore. It was nine o'clock and Venus looked down from the clock-tower. Of course I abandoned my plans immediately – it was not without reason that Napoleon fought no battles and Bismarck shrank from entering into agreements on a Friday.

Today, hardly a week later, I am as I said no longer willing to save Boris's neck. The omens at least are auspicious this time, not to say ideal for a day of judgement, since it is Jupiter who from the niche aloft watches over the course of events. To him who is the protector of justice and virtue, also called Light-Bringer, I shall make my sacrifice, thus following the ancient custom of magistrates and victorious generals. With renewed energy my fingers close upon the wooden shaft; the trembling in my hand has almost gone. Secretly I hope that my scheme will win the approval of outsiders too.

I did not hear the footfalls on the stairs, but an indefinable feeling tells me that I am no longer alone in my room. 'Are you going to see me off to Alba Iulia tonight, Andrei?' The smile on my sister's face implies some doubt. Absently I nod my head. Of all my former allies Eva alone has remained faithful; one could go so far as to call her my accomplice. But just now her presence is most inopportune. Lost in thought I return to the clock-tower, right up to the gallery from where – the very next moment – young Romanov is going to throw himself into the deep. Good-bye Boris! Relentlessly, almost of its own accord, my carved penholder has begun to fly across the pages.

Mark Tilton

They Came By Night

Early to bed but never a good night's sleep, for every night they would come at him, trying to catch him unawares. 'You're only as young as you feel'... 'It's being so cheerful that keeps me going'... 'There's nowt s'queer as folk'... 'Laugh, and the world laughs with you. Cry, and you cry alone.' Clichés would crawl out from under the furniture, from the dust-filled corners, and stalk him, before pouncing on the bed and suffocating him with tired expressions. There was no escape.

But on this night he was better prepared. A familiar creak from the shadows signaled a platitude beginning its creeping ascent from the floor up the foot of the bed. He could make out its pale hands fumbling the bedpost. It had his scent. It was only a matter of time. As it grasped the bed-rails, beginning to heave itself up, straining under its own hackneyed weight, he brushed the dangling night-cap from his face, took up the shot-gun he'd placed close by the bed, cocked the trigger, took careful aim... and fired.

All went blank. For the rest of his life the blunder would haunt him in the form of a limp — for the platitude had been his own foot. There was no cartoon-character rubber-ball recovery for him, oh no. He was flesh and blood. From then on, each stiff-legged step was confirmation to all who knew him that those lame expressions had been the creations of his own dull imagination. All sympathy was lost.

He was shunned by his so-called friends. His family disowned him, even his beloved children, for whom — before the incident — he could do no wrong. As a cherry-red sun set on his fading happiness, he saw no option but to leave, and set out for a new life beyond the purple horizon. 'The sun will come up tomorrow,' he told himself, 'come what may.'

Graeme Craig

6 May 1983

Memories from the night before dropped like bombs, flashes of events and conduct that could never be explained by right-minded people. Unfathomable, juvenile behaviour that was completely unaccountable. Nevertheless, he was at peace. The previous night would be the last time he would have to conceal drunkenness from his parents. Today, on his eighteenth birthday, as far as Archie Liddel was concerned, he became a man; drinking in pubs was now legal. And anyone that had a problem with that could go fuck themselves.

What is harder to accept, for a boy of eighteen at least, is that it can be a complex business to be a man; maturity comes with age, but maturity in itself is not intrinsically linked with manliness. In the First Epistle of Paul to the Corinthians, he famously states the need to leave behind childish things. This was Paul's contrived way of telling the ancient Greeks to focus on the eternal over the temporal and that maturity should allow this change of focus to happen more easily. But in Paul's upbringing, maturity was bestowed on him by his elders at an early age with the bar mitzvah, a ceremony which predicates that a boy becomes subject to the commandments; that's what bar mitzvah means, son of the commandments.

For Archie, legal clarity defines the adult man when he reaches the age of sixteen, albeit with some provisos. The legislated age of maturity means that one can leave home, engage in a contract; loss of parenting rights for the parents; a right to full time employment; marriage; sex; change your name; have a passport; and military service, albeit with parental consent. However, a man's first legal drink in a bar will not happen for another two years.

Those two long years had elapsed and Archie was hung-over. It was all he could do to get up that morning, open the birthday cards and presents, grin his gratitude at the money and record tokens, the obligatory shirt or jumper chosen by his mum, a horrendous fashion disaster he would have to wear that night. All the same, he was pleased to make it to this milestone with his crapulence escaping discovery by his parents, or more specifically by his dad. Charles Liddel was a man that many described as uncompromising.

The initial fuss over, he lay on the couch to sleep off his grinding hangover. Archie knew that he needed to rest if he was to go out that night and do it all over again. Starting off in The Argyll and Sutherland on the corner of Inverkip Street and Bruce Street, it was a man's pub; it didn't even have a ladies' toilet. The Argyll was typical of the old style bars found in Greenock; comprised of a small lounge, saloon and a snug where you could buy a carry-out. Etched on the glass of the snug door was the misnomer, *Family Dept.* What normally happened in the Family Department was that children waited there for their fathers to finish getting pished or for their money to run out; usually sent by their mothers to get their *faither hame fur his tea,* the child would chaperone the old man as he lurched back, hoping the old bastard would collapse on arrival. Otherwise there would be a risk of violence; one word out of turn and somebody would get fucking leathered.

Inside, the circumference of the horseshoe bar was marked by a stone gutter where regulars were known to piss or vomit. You could throw up a bad pint into the gutter where you stood then immediately order your next. Convenience is everything when drink is the priority. Like many pubs in the town, the Argyll served fortified wine; frowned upon by decent people, but the drug of choice for those that needed a cheap high, inevitably leading to an inhuman low. The general belief was that it was mainly imported from South Africa in the form of a solid jelly, melted down and bottled.

Snow has such significance for Eskimos they apparently have two hundred words to describe it. Fortified wine holds similar significance in Greenock: *The jake, vino calypso, lanliq or lannie, spoil the party, the screech, buckie, who are you looking at, electric soup*; and the brands available: Four Crown, Lang's Liqueur, Buckfast Tonic Wine, Thunderbird, Emva Cream, VP, and the legendary Eldorado. Eldorado was like Hoover; a particular brand of a product and often confused as the product itself.

Fancy an El D?

Aye. I could murder a Four Crown.

Archie and his best friend Robert Campbell favoured the Argyll for a number of reasons: it was en route to town, so it was a good place for a cheap pint before going on to a club. All forms of life could be witnessed in the saloon of the Argyll. On Friday nights a fishwife would come in selling Arbroath Smokies from a wicker basket. But the big attraction for Robert was the particular brand of fortified wine on offer; Walnut Brown. Despite the many warnings he received from his father, Archie was happy to succumb to peer pressure and ride shotgun with Robert in the pursuit of oblivion. He just assumed he should be like his friend and saw no need to be any different. Besides, it felt like fun. And it never felt more like fun than when they drank Walnut Brown. Sometimes celebrated to the tune of *Golden Brown* by the Stranglers:

> *Walnut Brown*
> *When in the town*
> *We drink it down*
> *Never a frown*
> *With Walnut Brown*

Archie woke to hear his parents whispering in the kitchen.

'Go on. It'll be good for you both.'

On the TV flickered an old episode of *The Waltons*. The rapacious young John-Boy was to accompany his father for the first time on the annual hunting trip to bag the Thanksgiving turkey. It was supposed to be an honour when a father took his son on the turkey shoot; a rite of passage. John-Boy was deemed old enough to handle a gun and man enough to use it. With his father and the other men, John-Boy headed up Walton's Mountain.

'Just a quick drink. Where's the harm?'

John-Boy gets sight of a turkey. Sensitive boy that he is he can't pull the trigger. Looking the thing in the eye down the barrel of a rifle seemed unfair. What chance did the bird have? When he tries to explain to his dad the old man claims to understand. But the other guys on the shoot were astonished. John-Boy could sense the weight of his father's disappointment; the day should've been a proud moment for both man and boy.

'Fur Chrissake, Elsie. The boy disnae want to sit in a pub wi' me.'

Later in the hunt, a grizzly bear attacks John-Boy's dad. Only John-Boy witnesses the incident and only he can save his old man. He raises his rifle and tries to train the gun on the bear, not easy as the beast wildly paws at his father. This is an enormous test for any marksman as the bear and man roll around on the forest floor in frenzied attack.

'Go on Charley. Ye might enjoy yourselves.'

John-Boy puts the squeeze on the trigger and the bear drops. John Walton's life has been saved by his son. Hailed as a hero, his maturity had been secured by the kill.

'Och awright.'

Archie's dad comes out of the kitchen with his paper and sits in his chair. His mother hovers at the door drying her hands in the apron that seems permanently tied round her waist. Archie's pretty sure he knows what's coming and he likes the idea. He knows it was his mother's idea but he doesn't care. He also knows that his dad will make the suggestion when it suits him. When it looks like it's his idea.

'You meeting Robert, Archie?'

'Aye, but no fur ages.'

'I was thinking, if you like, we could nip out fur a drink or something? You know, like in a bar. A drink?'

'Aye, great! Whatever ye think. Great idea.'

'Ok then. Good. A drink. Ma boy's first legal drink.'

Archie's mother was delighted. She rushed through

the living room to the hall and they followed to find her holding their coats.

'Look at ma two boys. Going for a drink together.'

She handed over the coats then kissed each of them firmly on the cheek. Elsie Liddel meted out affection with such force it often felt like a mugging. Charles became flustered.

'Fur Chrissake, Elsie. Compose yersel'.'

The Rankin Park Social Club was chosen to mark the occasion. It faced the junction of Dunlop Street and Inverkip Street and consisted of a large dance hall and a small lounge. Through the lounge you could get to the snooker hall which had six tables. From there was a gym and a changing room. Behind the club lay a football pitch and then the hills rising up to and beyond Pennyfern Road. The pitch was the home ground for Belair Football Club. It was once rendered unplayable for a few weeks when someone used it to exercise a horse, the hooves digging up the turf and leaving it turned over like a ploughed field. The episode mystified locals for months; few had ever seen a horse unless Gary Cooper was on it.

To the left of the football pitch was Waverly Street, the houses backing on to the park with a grandstand view. To the right of the field the ground rose up to a zen garden. Surrounded by hedgerow and with its own pavilion it was the Rankin Park Bowling Club. Archie loved it there, the stillness, the tranquillity. On the lawn he felt isolated from the world. He never played bowls, none of that shite; he just thought it was a nice spot.

Archie sat at a Formica table in the lounge awaiting his father's return from the bar. He was surrounded by a collection of men repeatedly lifting pint glasses and tumblers to their lips, passively ingesting their chosen sedative; conversation was kept to a minimum. For a Social Club this was one of the most unsociable scenes Archie had ever witnessed. He was eighteen and anything was possible. A lifetime of opportunity was ahead of him. But as he looked around him he worried that he saw the future: his own future. He wondered if he would ever get to that place where drinking would feel like a turgid necessity. These men seemed content to Archie, passing their afternoons numbing themselves to life.

With one hand resting on the table top, he rubbed the edge with the tip of his thumb; it felt rough to his touch. The veneer trim from the edge of the table had long since gone exposing the chipboard underneath. Over time the cheap fibreboard had absorbed a huge volume of alcohol causing distortion at the surface. He then recognised the same characteristics in the clientèle around him.

The youngest guy in the club, Archie was time rich, but he felt urgency gripping him. It shook him and caused him to fear for his ambitions. As he sat quietly in the lounge he knew that adventure was happening elsewhere. Experience was being exploited by other people in other locations. What Archie wanted for his life was not happening in the Rankin Park Social Club. He wasn't even sure it was happening in Greenock.

Nevertheless, his primary concern was to enjoy this rite of passage his mother had engineered. Partake of a man's drink with his dad in a man's surroundings. Exchange banter as equals. Leave behind the limitations of their previous father/son relationship and embark on a new grown-up association.

His father appeared. 'Let me sit there son. I like tae face the door.'

Archie sloped round to the other side of the table.

'And for Chrissake sit up straight. Ye look like ye need a rocket up yer arse.'

He placed a pint of lager in front of Archie, sat down and tipped his glass over to slowly pour his small bottle of Sweetheart Stout. Archie lifted his drink and said 'Cheers!'

His dad threw him a look of disapproval. He was waiting for his stout to settle before he would raise his glass and propose a toast. He saw it as his job to salute his son on his birthday. Archie looked back at his father over the top of the glass and removed the lager from his lips and placed the pint back on the table top. He felt his birthday treat losing its veneer.

'Well son, I guess yer now a man in the eyes of some but you'll always be ma boy. I held you in ma arms eighteen years ago today as a brand new baby. Something I thought I'd never know. It felt good and terrifying aw at the same time, but I felt like a man. I had a job I liked, a wife I cherished, and a family to provide for. If you're lucky maybe one day you'll know what that feels like. Cheers.'

They lifted their glasses to drink, Charles concluding by theatrically hissing out a breath of satisfaction while Archie could only measure his disappointment at the occasion. He genuinely thought that this moment might be an opportunity for them to begin communicating with each other in a more meaningful way, as equals.

He thought about his dad's course in life. He conformed to the small town convention that was prevalent in Greenock; one education, one job, one wife, one family. If that was what it took to become a man then he wanted to choose another path, march to a different drum. But the rot was already setting in.

At eighteen, Archie was assessing his life, or rather dreading his future. He looked at his old man beside him as he fished in his pocket for cigarettes. His dad had never been out of the country, he didn't even have a passport. He'd lived his entire life in the same town and Archie was beginning to feel he would do the same. Greenock was a hard town; a hard working town of hard men, hard drinkers, hard luck and heartache. An urban sprawl that undulated along five miles of the south bank of the Clyde, the town resembled an unmade bed. A patchwork quilt of grey slate roofs disturbed by monolithic blocks of post-war housing solutions.

And the rain. It came to Greenock like the tide to the shore, a monotonous regularity that never failed to disappoint. The sky was continuously foreboding and looked as though it was covered by a layer of roof insulation. The rain fell in angry wet slaps of admonishment. It always fucking rained in Greenock.

But the town had a beauty that eighteen year-old Archie Liddel could not perceive. Where the unforgiving land met the mystery of the river, a chemical reaction fizzed along the edge. Every day fireworks glittered and sparked in the reflection on the oil that shimmered on the water. The energy and purpose of the town was seen at its best from the river. Local historian and poet, Daniel Weir once wrote:

Enbosom'd in a lovely bay
We see thy crowded mansions rise
While commerce, with her proud display
Arrests at once our wondering eyes

Greenock was a shipbuilding town. Archie was serving an apprenticeship in the yards where his father worked and his father before him. He was doggedly following the well trodden path that he was determined to avoid. The river flowed past the town while Archie remained static; a bulrush rooted in the mire of the local industry.

Archie's dad looked back at him with a freshly lit cigarette between his fingers. What do men say to each other? 'Did your dad do this with you? First legal drink?'

His dad froze, took a sideways glance at his son, stubbed out his cigarette, then turned to face Archie square on. 'Ma father's fondness for drink made him no father at all. All his life he prioritised whisky over the family. When ma mother had to scratch around for pennies to put food on the table for me and ma sisters, he always had money in his pocket for drink. A self-centred, inconsiderate soul, he was a violent, abusive man that only thought of his own selfish pleasures.

'When ah was twelve years of age he was found dead from an alcohol induced epileptic seizure. He was alone and face down in West Burn Street. He was jaundiced and malnourished. An autopsy showed his liver grossly enlarged, inflammation of the pancreas, heart disease and a malignant tumour the size of a tennis ball in his colon. His love of grain alcohol meant that he never saw me leave school and take up ma profession, never met yer mother or got to know any of his grandchildren.

'It meant that ah never knew the kind of experience that you and I are enjoying now. How's the lager?'

'It's a little flat.'

The silence returned. Archie thought 'There's never a grizzly bear around when you need one.'

He knew that this was just another day like any other. But he hoped that turning eighteen would mark a change in the way his father would regard him. He wanted to tell him this wasn't his first taste of alcohol. That he'd been drunk before and it hadn't killed him. That he'd had sex. That he'd had sex on the lawn of the Rankin Park Bowling Club. That he could get his own place to live, have children and go to war. That he was a man like him. But if Archie had changed his dad hadn't.

Sit up straight.

Ye need a rocket up yer arse.

You'll always be ma boy.

If yer lucky maybe one day you'll feel like a man.

Archie was on the same one-way street he always travelled with his father. Respect flowed in one direction only. Archie was tired of this routine. He knew that the thin end of the wedge did not get any thicker because your old man bought you a pint in the Rankin-fucking-Park Social-fucking-Club. He wanted the ritual to end. But he failed to understand that this rite of passage marked an important transition in both their lives. For Charles, as a husband and father the dual role brought responsibility that he was more than equal to. But now his son was becoming a man, he was just a husband, no longer needed as a father figure, that position was now merely an ex officio role; a responsibility now lost. He would never again pick up his son in his hands and feel like a man.

Born in Greenock, in the West Central Lowlands of Scotland, one of Charles Liddel's earliest memories was of being taken down to the Anderson shelter when the air raid sirens wailed; his dad staying put while the family scrambled to make sure their blackout curtains were closed and make their way to the basement bunker that served all those in the close. Charles would be sick with terror while his father sat in his armchair, nonchalantly blowing smoke from his roll-up and having a wee nip. Not even the Luftwaffe could prevent Charles's dad from being a gallous bastard.

'Fuck 'em.'

This was Charles Snr's idea of defiance. Charles Jnr thought he was a fool. He had a fool for a father and the biggest joke of all was that he carried his name.

It was May 1941; the Greenock Blitz, two nights of intense bombing which decimated large parts of the town. Around fifty bombers targeted the shipyards that attached the town to the River Clyde, but serious damage was also incurred in East Crawford Street, Belville Street, and other parts of the east end. More than half of Greenock's homes suffered damage with around one thousand completely destroyed. Over the two nights, two hundred and eighty people were killed and over twelve hundred injured.

This was the second night of the blitz. Everyone knew the heavy price Greenock had paid the night before, but Charles's dad still played the big man upstairs in the sitting room. Living at the end of Ladyburn Street, Charles always enjoyed the benefits of staying round the corner from Cappielow Park, home of his beloved Morton Football Club. Saturday afternoons spent running round to the Sinclair Street end and getting a punt over the wall so you could see the game for free. If it was a mid-week game Charles could listen to the match from his bedroom. He could tell exactly what was happening from the noise of the fans. When they scored, it seemed as though the crowd exploded outside his bedroom window. He loved that roar.

But this wasn't a midweek game. The house was almost as close to the shipyard as it was to Cappielow. With his sisters he huddled next to his mum in the shelter with his eyes tightly closed. At that moment Charles wished he lived anywhere but Ladyburn Street. As they feared for the whistling of the first bombs his mother could feel her only son rigid with fear. She cowed to his ear and softly began singing his song:

Charlie is my darlin,
my darlin, my darlin,
Charlie is my darlin,
the young Chevalier

And then it came. It fell so close, thundered so loud, the bomb destroyed half of Ladyburn Street. The bunker seemed to jump at the blast. In the silence following the explosion, masonry dust seeped from cracks and seams around the shelter. Now Charles felt his mother stiffen 'Oh Charley!'

It hadn't occurred to Charles that his dad might be caught in the blast, but now it did. He didn't know how to think about it. He didn't know anybody that didn't have a father. But he didn't know anybody that had a father like his.

Everyone in the bunker went quiet. Mrs Jessop, their next door neighbour squeezed his mother's hand. They could hear more bombs falling but they became remote, turning into muffled bursts of paper bags. Despite the ongoing blitz, the silence thickened.

The door of the bunker exploded open with Charles Snr flying in and landing in the middle of the shelter on his hands and knees. Gone was the swagger that normally accompanied the entrance of Charles Liddel. He was ashen-faced and gasping for air. His back arching and dropping with every breath that rattled in his bronchi. After a few moments he lifted his head and looked at the shocked expressions that faced him and said 'Did ye hear it? Nearly landed in ma fucking drink!'

Everyone roared in hysterical laughter. Tears were filling the eyes of the women who were desperately trying to control their pelvic floors, fearful of an accident. Men were slapping Charles on the back and dragging him up to a seat. Children giggled at the swear word. Mother smiled and shook her head and everyone laughed and laughed. Everyone laughed except young Charley.

He wondered just how close that bomb came.

'So have you had lager before?'

Archie looked at his dad to see if there was any menace in the question but he was delving into his jacket pocket again for his cigarettes. He often thought that it was a miracle that his dad never caught on to his boozing. But Archie reassured himself that he was too fly; always got home after his parents went to bed. Always had a wee story for where he was the night before.

'Some o' the boys have had a pint an' said it was alright.'

As he held his lighter to the cigarette in his mouth Charles looked directly at Archie over the hand he cupped around the flame 'If the boys said strychnine was alright would ye drink that?'

Archie's heart sank. This was not the time for a lecture. This was not the time for his old man to live up to expectations and disappoint. To let him feel they might be getting somewhere and then return to his default setting. He didn't fear his dad but he feared what might become of their relationship. He didn't want to be his dad's boy anymore. He had done that already.

'Listen son, ye know am no' a drinker. Tae be quite honest this wisnae ma idea. But ah know you're yer ane man now. Ah might no' like ye bevvyin' but ah know ah cannae stop it.'

Archie was stumped for a response. His father had just called him a man and all he could do was to clam up like a diffident child.

'Jist one thing Archie, ye might no' know it but yer mother disnae sleep till ye get hame at night. And that means ah get nae sleep wi' her sitting up in bed fretting.'

Archie felt the blood rising up his neck to his face.

'Sober men don't come crashing intae the house the way you do, son. All I ask is ye never gie yer mother anything tae worry aboot. Dae ye know what I'm saying son?'

Charles Liddel's relationship with drink was influenced by his relationship with his father, but he knew that this should not be the yardstick by which he measured the partaking of alcohol in others. Although he never developed a taste for it himself he knew it would be dictatorial to demand the same of his son. Archie never expected this from his dad. He couldn't believe how good he was being; he never thought that he could be so accepting of something that had been so abhorrent to him. His dad was a bigger man than he ever thought possible. 'Ok faither.'

They sat in silence for a moment. Both thinking about the clean slate they now shared. Charles puffing plumes of blue/grey smoke in to the air. Archie understood that his dad had offered him an olive branch. But it came at a price – *Don't be a fucking idiot and we can forget any previous indiscretions.* Archie thought he could live with that.'Ye know ah thought I came in quietly at night. Thought ah was being clever.'

Charles Liddel looked at his son for a stunned moment then threw his head back to guffaw disbelief. Archie was crestfallen that the past months of covert drinking had been so easily exposed by the old man. But he was pleased they were laughing about it. It felt good. He'd rarely seen his dad so unselfconscious. But such joy was not usually a feature of the Rankin Park Social Club and he attracted the looks of the docile regulars in the small lounge.

'Ok faither. It's no' that fucking funny.'

Archie met Robert at the end of Mount Pleasant Street, two minutes from the Argyll. Robert had been legal drinking for five months already but neither of them felt comfortable meeting inside the saloon. It was best to show a united front and enter together; confidence in numbers.

'Look at wee Archie; yer all grown up.'

'Ok, behave yersel.'

'Gimme a kiss.'

'Oh fuck off.'

'C'mon! A birthday kiss fur ma wee Archie.'

'Jist fuck off, please.'

Robert's mock affection was an immense source of amusement to him, but it served another purpose other than just annoying his best friend. It allowed him to demonstrate a level of physical warmth that was acceptable between men. Between men that were close friends but not arse-bandits. There was nothing sinister in Robert's mock affection; just genuine affection. He grabbed Archie by the scruff of the neck and planted a kiss on his forehead. *Mmwaah!*

They found a spot in the saloon and Robert leaned in to the bar between the assembled bevvy merchants. He quickly got the attention of the barmaid, a woman that must've been sixty five at least, trying without any success to look fifty. Heavy make-up caked on a face dried and cracked from a life time of Woodbine addiction. Dyed chestnut brown hair incongruously perched on her head. Archie knew that she only worked there for the company. To hear and re-peat the same gossip night after night. Looking forward to

135

her staff drink at the end of the evening when the bar was closed and the till cashed. The mere sight of this woman depressed Archie, but for Robert, it was an opportunity to practise charm. 'Two lagers and two Walnut Browns, and one fur yersel darling.'

Archie wondered where Robert got his confidence. He knew it was mostly bravado but it still impressed him. He didn't know that without him around Robert shrivelled a little. He needed a straight man. Somebody that made him feel better about himself. Not that Archie played Estragon to Robert's Vladimir. But physically they were different. While Archie was slight Robert was athletic. He looked strong. He liked to work out and liked the way it made him feel, the way exercise transformed his body. Archie was the shorter of the two and this was important to Robert. He felt powerful. He felt capable.

Robert was a junior insurance clerk for Fordham and Buchan, a broker on Jamaica Street. He was confident that he was going places, that he had a future outside the regular Greenock life plan. School, shipyards, married, dead; that wasn't for Robert Campbell. He often liked to remind Archie that he had risen above the torpid normality on offer to Clydeside men. 'Archie, ah always thought you would stay oot o' that shite. Ah remember in school ah thought ye were different. Everybody did.'

'Is that a compliment?'

'Och, ye know what ah mean. Aw the pricks in school had their futures mapped oot fur them, jist doing whit their auld boys done, nae hope, nae imagination, nae options. But here you are – a grease monkey in the yards next tae yer faither.'

Archie's hatred of this subject was the thing that made Robert return to it. 'Allow me tae put ye straight on a few things, Rab. Ah'm no' a grease monkey, ah'm an engineer.'

'Apprentice'.

'Aye ok, an apprentice engineer. Ma faither's no a grease monkey either, he's a coppersmith and we don't work next tae each other. And ah know it's shite around here, ah know it's shite in the yards and ah know ah need tae dae something aboot it, but ah also know that denying people rightful payment on their insurance claims at Bore 'em and Fuck 'em disnae mean the start of a brilliant career.'

Robert took exception to Archie dismissing his career choice when he was only trying to offer his friend advice. 'Ma turn to put you straight on a few things, Archie. Fur a start, it's no Bore 'em and Fuck 'em; it's Fordham and Buchan.'

'Pardon me.'

'Secondly, genuine, bona fide claims will always be processed and paid without question.'

'Fucking sure they will ya big, lying shitebag.'

'And lastly, ah've never said ah've got it all worked oot. But a year frae now ah'll be a fully fledged insurance clerk.'

'Oh just imagine it? Fly, Robert, fly.'

'Aye, fucking laugh, but ah'll be on a decent salary, company car, pension, benefits. Ah'll have choices. Whit will you have Archie? If ye huvnae lost an eye or a hand as a result of some health and safety fiasco, or died from Weil's disease because yer up tae yer knees in rat piss, or been kept on strike for weeks on end thanks to the union's archaic conspiracy theorists, ye might jist have the energy tae go cap-in-hand tae yer boss and beg fur some overtime. Fuck that!'

At this point Archie just wants to change the subject. 'Now ye put it that way, Robert, ye've made me realise how fucking happy ah am that ah'm no a junior insurance clerk.'

'Fuck you, Archie. Your problem is that ye think ah've joined the establishment. But look at ye; yer old man left a trail of footprints from school right intae the shipyards and like a fucking lemming you followed him right in. Like every other bawbag in this fuckin' toon.'

Robert and Archie had gone over this discussion in various formats many times, but it always ended the same way. His best friend confirming what he already knew.

Robert reached over the throng passing back lager and wine. Two old men hampered Robert's access to the bar and had started to sing. The would-be crooners were murdering the old McHugh/Adamson tune, *A Lovely Way to Spend an Evening*.

> *This is a lovely way to spend an evening*
> *Can't think of anything I'd rather do*
> *This is a lovely way to spend an evening*
> *Can't think of anyone as lovely as you*

The two linked arms as they serenaded each other. One had his cock out to pish in the gutter. Round the other side of the horseshoe bar somebody had already started a song of their own and was obviously more than a little peeved to discover that he wasn't the only show in town. He increased his volume:

> *Armoured cars and tanks and guns*
> *Came to take away our sons*
> *But every man will stand behind*
> *The Men behind the Wire*

Sectarian sentiments were strong in towns like Greenock. This was an old Paddy McGuigan song that described the raids by British soldiers and the Black and Tans resulting in Irish men being randomly interned without charge or trial at Long Kesh prison camp; the men behind the wire. A rebel tune that galvanised support for the IRA, it was well known in central Scotland where decades of hatred had evolved between Rangers and Celtic, Protestants and Catholics, Billys and Tims, Blue-noses and Fenians.

This vocal uprising roused the attention of a belligerent proddy, a big ugly fucker with a Red Hand of Ulster tattoo on his fore-arm. He responded with a rendition of the loyalist anthem, *The Sash My Father Wore*. Before he could get into his stride the barmaid screamed intervention. 'That's enough! We don't want any a that shite in here!'

A begrudging silence befell the other side of the bar; however Sinatra and Crosby continued to inform everyone what a lovely fucking evening they were having:

> *A casual stroll through a garden*
> *A kiss by a lazy lagoon*
> *Catching a breath of moonlight*
> *Humming our favourite tune*

Robert was now beside Archie and keen to employ his acerbic wit. 'Well my son, tonight I'm determined that your transition in to manhood should be celebrated in fine style. When on this day you change from being an adolescent, inept, fumbling boy, into an assertive, worthwhile, man of the world: A homme du monde. Forgive me if ah get emotional Archie, but last night when I watched ye spew up yer Pernod and blackcurrant in the street, as the purple vomit meandered its way into the gutter, I said tae masel "Tonight ma wee pal is a child, he throws up as a child, he knows fuck all like a child; but tomorrow he will become a man and put away childish things. And throw up like a man".'

'Is that the fucking bible?'

'Who knows? Anyway, enough o' that shite. Happy birthday, son. Ah wis gonnae get ye a wee pressie but ye know how things are. Ah mean ah did get ye something, but I liked it so much ah kept it fur masel. Smell it? Paco Rabanne. Gorgeous, eh? Oh! An' by the way, ye owe me two quid fur the taxi last night.'

'Remind me, Rab, why are we friends?'

The two laughed, clinked their wine tumblers and simultaneously necked their Walnut Brown. A slick of sticky, sweet venom burned down their throats. They no longer winced at this ritual but they still felt the sense of impending danger that came with such volatile liquor. They stood at the precipice of their own unhinged behaviour spawned from the amniotic sludge of fortified wine. There would be no outbreak for three or four hours, but very quickly they would feel the indelible confidence of champions swelling in their chests; newly ingested self-assurance that would allow them to wreak havoc with hopeful impunity.

But for now, there was only one thing to do. Take a

gulp of lager and extricate the taste of Walnut Brown.

Despite Robert's desire to celebrate in style, Saturday night would follow the same format as always; a quick stop off in The Regal Bar before heading to The Cathcart. It was a routine that served them well. Robert was at the bar again while Archie went to the toilet. As he stood at the urinal he could sense his descent into the miasma of unforgiving crapulence, the pall of jellied wine congealing and forming a feculent slurry in his mind. He peered at the graffiti-covered wall and tried to find something new, something different from the usual profane malevolence; something a little more Oscar Wilde than the routine animalistic bill of fare. And then he saw it; five words of comic genius. *Pakora Joe farts like fuck*.

For the Regal Bar something a little more sophisticated than Walnut Brown and lager was required. Robert had Archie's Southern Comfort and lemonade waiting for him when he returned from the toilet. Archie took the drink from his friend but before he savoured any he needed to get something off his chest before communication became impossible. 'Why don't we get a flat together?'

'Archie, is this a proposal?'

'I'm serious, why don't we? Am tired o' living at hame. Independence, Rab. That's what we need. An' I don't mean in fucking Greenock either. A flat in Glesga. Imagine it? You an' me in the big smoke, bringing women back, having parties. Doing whatever the fuck we like when we fucking like.'

'Aye that's right, ironing whenever we like, washing

dishes and dusting and cleaning. And don't get me started on paying bills; rent, rates, gas, leckie. I'm sick o paying ma mother pennies fur keep money. It leaves me far too much disposable income tae fritter away on things ah like. Fuck it, Archie. I'm going hame tae pack ma stuff right noo.'

Archie knew his idea was being dismissed without due consideration. 'Dae ye have tae be a prick aboot it? Ah jist think there's a better way a life fur us. Ah want tae feel that am ma ane boss. I've had enough of the old man and his shite aboot "ma hoose, ma fucking rules".'

'Listen Archie, yer forgetting something. A place in Glesga? We both work in Greenock. Yer no making any sense. Ah like tae come hame and ma mother's got ma tea ready, ma shirts ironed when ah need them. It's because we pay pennies tae live at hame that we can enjoy the kind of experience that you and I are enjoying now.'

Archie felt the argument leave him. Partly because he knew Robert was right, but more so because he wanted to avoid further opportunity for his friend to sound like his father. He felt impotent.

'C'mon Archie. Stop being such a miserable shite and drink up. There are women waiting at The Cathcart that want tae be Liddelled. So ah better get you over there or they'll be disappointed.'

They arrived inside The Cathcart just before the 11:00 curfew: in Greenock all premises with a late license could not legally permit entry after eleven. There was something seamy and exciting about getting into The Cathcart. It was in Watt Place; a small dimly lit lane off Cathcart Street.

The first few minutes inside the club were electrifying. Dominated by a large rectangular dance floor in the centre of the hall, the narrow entrance was dark as the Earl of Hell's waistcoat. They went to the bar at the far end by splitting up and circumnavigating the floor on either side. This approach allowed them to survey the entire club, see who was around and decide the best viewpoint to return to once drinks were acquired.

Archie was first to reach the bar and order two bottles of lager. Things were getting difficult for him now. His words were slurring badly and he struggled to hear the barmaid over the music.

Robert arrived and Archie handed him his bottle. Archie said, 'Ah saw a couple o' lassies frae school? Gemma Morrison. Did you no' lumber her at the leaving dance?'

Robert was cool in response. 'Been there done that. Thanks fur the warning anyway.'

'Warning?'

'Never mind. C'mon.'

They found a spot near the stairs leading to the toilets. This vantage point meant that sooner or later they would see every girl in the club as they inevitably made their way to the loo. It was at this point that the Cathcart began to lose its appeal for Archie. Making eyes at women on their way to the shithouse was not his idea of celebrating his birthday in style; Robert by his side assessing every girl that passed, flashing his shit-eating grin and hoping for a response. Archie knew that like him, Robert was losing his optimism rapidly. Drinking Walnut Brown girds one for greatness. Or more realistically it prepares you for extremes.

However opportunity rarely matched their expectations.

Then the moment they waited for arrived, the floor filler that played every Saturday night: The Snake. The 1968 Al Wilson number was the song that set the Cathcart apart from every other club in town. Sure, you still had to endure all the shite from the charts ad nauseam. But when this vintage hit pumped out of the PA system, the club came alive.

> *Take me in oh tender woman*
> *Take me in for heaven's sake*
> *Take me in tender woman*
> *Sighed the snake*

Robert and Archie put down their drinks and made their way to the edge of the floor. It took awhile for their eyes to focus on the seething mass and select their kill; like two hyenas waiting for an opportune moment to come down the hill and scavenge the remains. Archie spotted two attractive young women dancing together and Robert, seemingly looking at the same girls said, 'Those two, c'mon.'

He set off towards them but Robert wasn't referring to the same prey as Archie. He was already in the thick of the crowd heading towards his target when he saw his friend wander off. He reached through the bodies and grabbed Archie's shoulder yanking him back on course. But he pulled Archie too hard making him crash into himself and propel him into a New Romantic kid that was dancing flamboyantly behind. Pointy shoes, sharp suit with sleeves rolled up and shirt buttoned up to the neck. No tie. Hair shaved in at the sides with a long fringe blow dried to curl down over his eyes. It wasn't important for this kid to see anybody as long as everyone could see him.

Robert slurred an apology which the New Romantic was raising his open hands, palms outward, to accept. Archie instinctively knew that his help was required. He lunged forward and landed a punch just below the New Romantic's fringe. His nose shattered on impact. Archie's body weight carried him forward again and he had to hang onto the boy's jacket to stay upright. But the lad buckled under the weight and they both hit the floor in a tangle. They rolled around trying to get to their feet and other dancers soon followed them down. The music stopped, the lights came on and security rushed the floor.

Robert had Archie propped up against the sandstone facade of the Trustee Savings Bank on Cathcart Street. Archie was covered in New Romantic blood. 'What's your fucking problem tonight?'

Archie didn't know how to answer.

'Some fucking birthday. Ah hope yer fucking happy? We're fucking fucked now.'

Archie wanted to explain. 'Ah don't know how much longer ah can do this.'

'Do what?'

'This.'

'Ye mean The Cathcart?'

'Naw, everything.'

'Fur fucks sake, Archie.'

Robert was at the end of his tether. *You need a fucking rocket up your arse.*

The birthday was over. It was after midnight and with the curfew there nothing else to do but to make their way home. It was now the 7th May; the anniversary of the birth of the late Archibald MacLeish, a lawyer and Pulitzer Prize winning writer. Archie's mother's maiden name was MacLeish and it was his middle name too. Staggering home in the dark the road home seemed desperately lonely to Archie, a long slow crawl towards the end of the world. Was it possible his namesake felt the same sense of despair when he wrote his poem *The End of the World* ?

> *There in the sudden blackness the black pall*
> *Of nothing, nothing, nothing — nothing at all.*

Marie Florence

Brown Bear

He used to be the first one out of the den
after the long winter hibernation
hungry lean his coat a sleek glossy brown
wide nostrils gulping green April air
scenting the salmon leaping upstream
the wild raspberries growing down by the creek
smarter than the average bear

Nowadays he's difficult to rouse
it's early May and he's still drowsy
his eyes red-rimmed no spring in his step
his coat rough as some moth-eaten rug
nursing a sore head sluggish listless
so browned off he can barely muster a hug
growling about his hay fever

I have measured out my life in pints of Guinness

Go on gel get that down yer it puts 'airs on yer chest!
Nana Florrie insisted giving me my first Guinness
I'm standing on a table at The Eagle, Hoxton Street
lisping *Slow Boat to China* and *Ain't She Sweet*
I recoil at the sour brown bitterness
spit it out all over my new blue velvet dress

Scarlet Fever

Dawn calls out shepherds' warnings
yet I find myself back in the room
where I was lost. It's shrunk into a closet
condensed like a tin of Carnation milk
She shined the lino with Cardinal polish
soaked plum pudding in ruby port
every week from autumn 'til Christmas Eve
Rose floral disinfectant failed to mask
the sour reek of the sick bowl under the bed.
A bottle of sticky codeine cough syrup
glowed dully in the ruddy light of smouldering coals.
My throat raw as lamb's liver, iron bands
stifled my breath, muffled my cries
when I heard Mr. Wolf, long pink tongue lolling,
panting outside the bedroom door.

Metamorphosis

I'm idling on my usual park bench watching
sticky chestnut buds uncrumple when I notice
that the colours are fading to a muted monochrome
daffodils are above eye level
and monumental magnolias loom.

I feel an irresistible desire to roll on a dead starling,
to squirm in squirrel piss mixed with fox musk,
to swallow the windy sky, my moist black snout
snuffling at piled up clouds spilling
an ocean of multi-layered scents

Ultrasonic frequencies flood my senses.
I circle searching for a familiar presence.
The fine hairs on my paw pads tremble when they detect
your step minutes before I feel the reassurance of your
hand.

Tardis

I remember her shine
as she stretched out her hand
my lost lens cradled
in her small palm

how I swung her up into my arms
puzzled at how she managed to find
something so light and transparent
in our untidy kitchen

how a chill
zipped up my spine when she explained
I just touched myself
and turned back the time

Last year I would have given an eye
to return the favour to be able to say
to her no not that way
I have been in the future

Outsider

Some of them in the village have been harping on
about how she's more harpy than harpist how she turned
vicious on whiskey at the last wake she played
how she pissed all over the widower's shoes but she's an
                                                        artist
like me fine-tuned overstrung temperamental complex

She painted my shapely body with leaping salmon
coiled in Celtic knots she ripples Ninja fingers
over the strings plucking fairy laments from clear air
weaves stately counterpoints through beaux stratagems
sends my voice soaring like a lark over falls of water

One lambent summer evening when the Solstice moon
melted like an acid drop into the loch she left me
down by the strand for the offshore breezes to strum
random Aeolian minor harmonies from the Spanish Main
chance windsongs that penetrated her trembling bones

154

Kay Gallwey

Home from Holiday

I badly need to get home
but cannot bear to return
for not only are the living
there to greet me,
but also the dead.
Returning opens old wounds,
ghosts jostle at the door,
shadows pass me
cats long gone press and weave
against the one
who wakes, stretches and yawns.

Layers of ghosts
crowd the kitchen
lounge on chairs
watch me put the kettle on.
Like an egg
cracked against the side
of a bowl
my heart breaks.

Elmer Diktonius

translated from Swedish by Jim King

Diktatorns grav

The Dictator's Grave

Spring
around the dictator's grave.
Gentle wind around the monument to violence,
stiff-legged, gigantic.
The evil that he did –
and the air still freezes
when his name is uttered –
is dust and ashes like him,
already sunk into oblivion.
Where is the dominion he created,
the wild eagles on his banner?
– Sparrows are nesting in the willow bushes.

Myriads of anemones
around the dictator's grave,
fragile blooms of a few hours
swaying in the wind.
He trampled on state and nations,
but this:
myriads of anenomies
around the last remains of violence –
thus the life-force
smiles out of spring's sunshine ground
at death's denial.

Hjältegravar

Graves of Heroes

Monument of granite and bronze:
figures, sword in hand,
dying youths, grieving homeland –
in squares and public gardens with flowerbeds
statues
that speak, scream, gleam:
graves of heroes! graves of heroes!
Cairns in the densest forest,
snow-covered, hidden away.
without stone, cross or name –
not even tended;
only a few unguessed at cairns.
Yet you can hear that forest whispering, playing,
forest of bark-bread, forest of timber:
graves of heroes! graves of heroes!

Södergran

Södergran

Star-catcher –
your net is aglitter
with the clamour of the gods
and the rustle of dead flowers.
Unborn you saw everything;
sick you cured the sound.
No one could beget the midges of
poetry
like you
lifelike
bloodsucking.

Vilhelm Ekelund

translated from Swedish by Jim King

Jag dikter för ingen

I sing for no one

I sing for no one –
for the wandering wind,
for the weeping rain,
my song is like the blast
that mutters and goes
through autumn's dark night
and speaks to the earth
and night and rain.

Gunnar Björling

translated from Swedish by Jim King

Nu släckes ljus

Now the light is fading

Now the light is fading and men are streaming out
it is evening, work is over
they stream across the square
black figures
and road and the shadows
window after window grows dim
mist lies grey on roofs
it is spring and peace
and evening
shadows are still streaming out
and light spreads over road and fields.

Här i ett land

This is a country

This is a country to live in
and sleep summer under trees
here by river and shore's edge
among the summer leaves and glades
rowing a boat naked.

Ett rum en bild

A room a picture

A room a picture on the wall
table chairs
and a heap
of paper
in disarray
and skimmed through
finger breeze
and traces of man.

Marie-Luise Kaschnitz

translated from German by Jim King

Genazzano

Genazzano at evening
Wintry
Glassy clip-clop
Of donkeys' hooves
Up to the steep hill town.
Here I stood by the fountain
Here I washed my bridal clothes
Here I washed my grave clothes
My face lay white
Under the black water
In the swaying foliage of the plane trees
My hands were two lumps of ice
Five icicles on each
Which made a tinkling sound.

Rosalía de Castro

translated from Galician and Spanish by Jim King

De soidás morríase

She was pining away

She was pining away
in the city, sighing for her village:
the houses with their walls cast a shadow over her,
and the towers and churches cast a shadow over her.

The paved streets, without
greenery and coolness, seemed to her
like graveyards where the dead
roamed abroad from sad sepulchres.

And the food tasted to her
of unsalted flour and hedge mustard,
and the little that she touched,
instead of nourishing, was killing her.

Sometimes – illusion or reality?
a sharp tang
of distant shores and pine groves reached her.

Then, she would climb to a high place and sit
gazing at the wide horizons,
and break into choking sighs,
shouting hoarsely, sobbing 'I am going away.'

And she left in haste ... no helping her. She went
with a mortal sadness gnawing at her.
Poor Rosa, she went away,
but... to the other Life.

Candente está la atmósfera

The air is a furnace

The air is a furnace
the fox explores the deserted road,
the crystal water
of the limpid stream turns brakish,
and motionless, the pine awaits
the inconstant kisses of the breeze.
An imposing silence
weighs down upon the countryside;
only the buzzing of an insect is heard
in the vast, damp shadows,
monotonous and constant
like a muffled death rattle.

This midday hour of summer,
how well it deserves the name of night,
when man, wearied of the fight
succumbs ever more
to matter's inert strength
and the infinite dread of the soul.

Return you nights of winter chill,
our old loves of former times,
return with your cruel frosts
to refresh the blood, scorched
by the sad and intolerable summer.

How sad...full of vine leaves and ears of corn.
Cold and heat, autumn and spring,
where...where is happiness to be found?
All seasons are beautiful
to those who bear joy within
but to the desolate and orphan soul,
there is no smiling or propitious season.

Vincenzo Cardarelli

translated from Italian by Jim King

Sera di Liguria

Ligurian Evening

The Ligurian evening rises
from the sea, slow, rose-tinted, ruin
of hearts in love and distant things.
Couples tarry in gardens
and one by one windows come alight
like so many theatres.
The tang of the sea emerges from the mist
that entombs it.
The churches on the shore look like ships
which are about to sail.

António Patrício

translated from Portuguese by Jim King

Em Primkipo

On Primkipo

The crystal autumn caught the island in a web
of Elysian light spun by the cypresses
into bronze green rocks; the pine woods rustled.
What did we hear? A flight of migrating storks,
grey, triangular, above the marine calm,
beating to time, caught up in the music,
as though in pursuit of a ghost through the air.
The beautiful harmony of wings stopped us in our tracks,
coming from the Black Sea, between gardens and houses.
And as though the migration, pink and grey farewell,
the adagio of parting spoke in you as well,
you clung to me confessing your terror:
it was death passing over our love.
A long time has passed, where are you now?
I wonder if the magic of that hour,
that flock of migrating storks,
pink and grey, vibrating in the sea air,
still flies and flies again within you, unreal miracle,
in the crystal autumn that caught the island in its web.

Jim King

Memories

I

At midday, the vine trellis where grapes
tasted of strawberries
dipped its shadow in the water.
The dragonfly came down to drink
breaking the surface with its motion.
I turned lizard on the sunwarm rim
of the watertank, stroking the stone like a tongue,
as the smell of garlic coiled round the jasmine.

II

With just the simplicity
of the swimmer gliding the waves
or the sun on the sea
it silently disappeared
leaving some doubt about
its having been at all.
They bolted and barred the doors
they fastened the windows down
filled in cracks
stopped up the chimney
and reinforced the roof
They tried to lure it

with soft music, wine
and other blandishments of
art and nature
But all to no avail
It left only a
silence behind
and they remained
gazing vacantly
into space, trying
to recall it.

Simon Pettifar

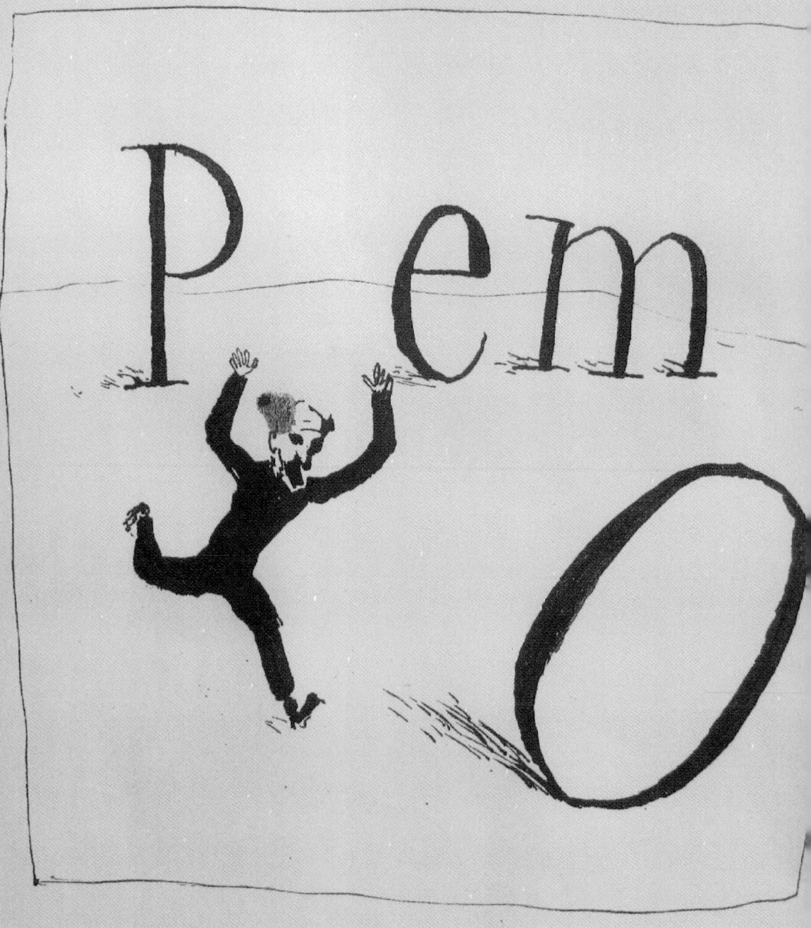

Pem
O

Turbulent Times

We are certainly living in turbulent times.
Jean-Paul Sartre – for or against?
Jacques Derrida – for or against?
Should we take a blowtorch to May '68?
Should we declare the anniversary of
the first Apollo moon landing a national holiday?
An international holiday? (Who could declare it?)
Punk rock – for or against?
Sigue Sigue Sputnik – for or against?
Janet Street-Porter – for or against?

Have the revolutionaries all become
little bourgeois capitalist pleasure seekers
without any faith in principles?
Have the cowboys and the outlaws? The Native Americans?
The ANC? Or haven't they?

The father has vanished, but why not the mother?
Isn't the mother really just a father, in the end,
and the father a mother? Is there anything post
post-post-modernism? Not yet, but there will be you say?

Why do young people not think any more?
(They do.) Why are children so unbearable?
(They are not.) Is it because of television,
or pornography, or comic books?

And women: are they capable of supervising male workers
on the same basis as men are?
Of thinking like men, of being philosophers?
Do they have the same brain, the same neurons,
the same emotions, the same criminal instincts?
Was Christ the lover of Mary Magdalene and if so
does this mean that the Christian religion is sexually split
between a hidden feminine pole and a dominant masculine

one?

Has the West become decadent? Has the East?
Are you for Spinoza, Darwin, Galileo, or against?
Are you partial to the United States?
Wasn't Heidegger a Nazi? Was Michel Foucault
the precursor of Bin Laden and Gilles Deleuze
a drug addict? Is the most interesting thing about Albert

Camus

his past in goal for Algeria?

Do these questions have any meaning for you?
Do they articulate your sense of the ills
of 'the present cultural moment'?
Do you want to hear any more of them?
Would you like to have a long conversation with someone
who feels the same way?

Is this insanity or mere hysteria (which would be bad
enough)?
Do you feel in need of a refuge?
Of earplugs? Of a hug?
Of a ten-day Vipassana Meditation course,

or half a lifetime as a Trappist monk
(like the young Louis Althusser, pre-uxoricide)?

Will we ever teach the body to lie?
God knows we try and try and try.
Her hand on mine, instructed to caress,
burns with falsity, does not know tenderness.

Come home, come down, come in,
come here. Kiss me
then lay your head upon my chest.
Rest.

Bryn Ddwynant

Novice

What woke me my first morning here
to look through glass
as into a dream,
through morning mist, fine rain,
and see at the first field's edge a lamb
half-fixed, her rear arcing side to side,
head stuck?

Then watching
heard her steady bleating through the wet:
continual alarm.

I pulled on jeans and someone else's boots,
stepped out into the blessing,
face-wetting rain,
and over the soft field to find her at the fence,
her pretty horned head thrust through and fixed.

I straddled her and held her; one fist thick with damp soft
wool
she calmed, and as her lips, one eye, turned
skyward by my hand I saw her horns would hold her still,

this way
or that, and I began to doubt I'd do it, like a dream.

But wire was worn away a moment then
re-formed, or it seemed so, and of a sudden out she fell,
paused a tiny moment then
sprang off, no glance or gratitude, and I looked over,
saw her kneel in fiery sunlight now beneath her Mum and
butt the milk into herself,

and felt happy, as if I'd done it.
I felt goodness in me,
felt a good shepherd who'd done his job.

On waking later our roles shifted with the day
turning about.
                        Were you the lamb,
Good Shepherd, or were you the wire?
Were you the weather or the fire?

Initiate

Four weeks later I'm checking the sheep.
One's flat down, eyes closed, barely breathing.
I forage for ivy, make a compact pan of it,
kneel and ram it through tight lips
and up against her teeth, far back.
She doesn't move.
I place my hands – slightly cupped, long trowels –

one beneath and one above her jaws,
and try to get her grinding.
When I stop moving my hands
she starts moving her jaws.
We continue like this awhile,
me having to push hard through her
clamped lips, she pausing, grinding,
grinding, pausing,
eyes closed, chin still to ground.
Later, eyes open, she'll nibble the ivy from my palm.

That evening I take the sugar beet that's been soaking.
As I stand on the gate I see her,
very lean but on her feet and grazing,
and she comes walking up the field to me,
stumbling, gently purposeful but very weak.
Gradually she nubbers up the beet, the bulk of it,
And of course my heart takes hope.
Though she backs off each time I move my hand towards
her head, doesn't like it if I try small pats
or strokes between her horns, she three times
lifts her face and gently, very very
gently, brushes the backs of my fingers with her nose,
the little hairs above her lips, and in this
she comes to me and I meet her.
The gift of this, my sensing her, stays with me
through the night.

But after eating she moves off and stands unnaturally.
I see and hear her guts twitch and heave,
her head hung down as she,

half-concentrating and half-suffering,
stands like one about to fall.

I wish I'd brought her in that night.

But while I backed away, unsure,
the flock came up and gathered round her
and I saw how she took on its energy in herself.
How strangely these animals are always merged,
or ailing. So I left, and hoped.

Heavy rain all night,
appalling me each time I wake.

Then morning at last, bright sun, rain blown away,
and I head out
to find her dead,
all gone.

Emmanuel

Where are you now?

In this only-absence, somehow still?

I seek that goodness
which brushed my fingers with her nose.
That's how we met,

in two incarnate creatures,
flesh and bone of sheep, of human being,
aided by these bodies, bodying.

And now?

You're here, still there,
Good Shepherd all in all
unseen but not unknown,
and summer's fire has turned to winter's fall
of snow upon the hills as I look out again
to Twmpa, Mynydd Troed, and forward
into Advent and beyond

Bryn Ddwynant, June/July – Pen y Bec, November 2008

A River Trip

'So we beat on, boats against the current, borne back ceaselessly into the past.'

He put the book down and leant back against the hard wooden slats of the bench. He could feel the edges of the narrow strips of wood sharp against his spine and against the muscles in his back. Stretching his arms out to either side, extending them along the top of the warm wood, he closed his eyes and tilted his head upwards so that the warmth of the sun fell directly onto his face.

He had read the book twice before but still its last line had come as a surprise. He wondered that he had forgotten it. He said the words over to himself once more, moving his lips. They were beautiful, he thought. And yet . . . Why did he suspect them so? The line was lyrical and lovely, melancholy and mysterious. But was it not too perfect, its balance of suggestiveness and precision too neatly achieved? He had thought so once. Now, saying the words over to himself a second time, they struck him as simple, clear, their meaning shorn of mystery. Only, he thought, why beat on?

With his eyes closed the motion of the boat was nearly imperceptible. Only the dull drone of its engine and the faint taint of diesel on the air told of it.

Why, he wondered, had he read the book again? When, the night before the arrival of his children, he had stood before the two short shelves of books in his room and looked calmly along them in order to select a new book to begin, what had made him choose, after all, the only book there which he had already read? And again he asked, why beat on? and wondered to himself whether it was that question which, without his knowing, had made him return to the book. But he had not been thinking about time; he had not even remembered that last sentence. He had remembered only the scene where the lovers are brought together again, brought together after a gap of five years during which they have had no contact with each other. That was what he had wanted, wanted to have again – that moment of tenderness and intimacy which exists for the reader – this he had remembered, or thought, now, that he had remembered – precisely because it is not described, is initiated – so delicately, with what delicate clumsiness on the part of the two principal actors – is initiated and then left to run its course outside the reader's purview; except that there is nowhere for it to run to, and there is nothing to propel it, and in its perfect moment it can only stand still and the reader, when he rejoins the lovers after standing outside in the rain with the one who has brought them together and then left them, sees only that, in his absence, it has come to pass, and when he re-enters their presence beholds it with a kind of quiet wonder. That was what he had wanted to have again.

The boat moved swiftly on. And that line of Gatsby's – a little later, when the party is over and she has not enjoyed it – that incredulous cry. Gatsby is right, he thought, of course you can. But who would *want* to repeat the past?

Something made him open his eyes. His two daughters were standing before him, giggling. Light streamed around the edges of their dark shapes.

'We crept up on you!' squealled the younger of the two girls.

'You did!' he replied, then quickly darted forward to tickle her. But she was too quick for him and swerved away, perfectly, giggling still.

'Daddy, will you play Split with us?'

He turned towards the older girl, 'Of course, but let's go inside, it'll be cooler there.'

The three of them descended the steep metal stairway into the belly of the boat and when they reached the deck he followed the two girls towards a table next to a large group of lounging teenagers. They sat, and as the older girl began to shuffle and then cut the cards and the younger girl watched her and stole shy glances of her own, he too looked over towards the other table at the lounging, animate mass of artifice and baggy fashion which sat sprawled around it: the baseball caps, the enormous trainers with their tongues lolling and their long laces, wide and flat, spooling around them; the wide khaki trousers, masterpieces of inconsequentiality in their plethora of pockets, loops and flaps, whose cuffs fell about the trainers in baggy folds and heaps; enormous shirts worn open and untucked over T- shirts; the girls sharp-eyed and vacant at the same time, looking younger than it was possible to be, their torsos tight in tiny tank tops and T-shirts, their thin arms bronzed and downy with pale hair. The table in their midst was a litter of cigarette packets, personal stereos, sunglasses, bottles of beer and cans of Diet Coca Cola.

'Ready, Daddy?'

He turned back to face his daughters, jolted by her clear, firm voice into a sudden awareness of the contrast between the older girl's resolute refusal to look over at the neighbouring table and his own lazy drift towards it, to which he had succumbed in no more than a moment. 'But she called me back,' he said to himself, and smiled at her.

It was only after they had begun their second game of cards that he noticed the older girl begin to allow herself soft, oblique glances over towards the teenagers.

It all looked unbelievably glamorous to them, he knew that. That was why they had chosen this table at which the three of them were now sitting – so as to be near that riot of louche independence and youthful, self-aware maleness, with its imitations of cool detachment as well as its sudden bursts of emotion and exclamation, jokes and laughter; its densely coded gesturing, the made-up faces of the young girls and all the litteringly attractive gadgetry and shiny paraphernalia of prosperous adolescence. He knew that, as far as his daughters were concerned, they were looking at the epitome of 'Cool'. Except that they were very careful not to look at it, or to be seen looking at it, at all.

But it was he, not his daughters, who found it difficult to give to their game even the small amount of attention which it required.

Why could he not picture his sister as a teenager? Why could he not see her in his mind's eye as she had been then? As if for clues he looked over once more at the lounging group as they smoked and laughed, threw things across the table to one another, kissed. He could remember how it felt to be in such a group; yes, he could, he could remember that. But he did not see his sister in any of it. They were close in age; but where was she?

'*Daddyyyyy*, it's your *turn*.' For the third or fourth time the older girl brought his attention back to the game. He smiled at her, felt the falseness in the smile and looked down at his cards; selecting one, he put it onto the pile between them. How had she worn her hair? Was it long or short? What sort of clothes had she liked to wear?

Why could he not see her?

The boat's horn sounded a loud blast once, twice, three times, and then there was a short announcement in German over the speaker system. The two girls watched him as he listened. 'We'll be there in three minutes,' he said, 'time to pack up.'

Two minutes later they were standing on the open deck again, watching the boatman in his bright blue workman's dungarees and black steel-capped boots as he stood patiently, ready to step off the boat and secure the heavy rope which he carried looped over his arm to one of the shining black metal bollards which lined the small quayside. They were the only passengers waiting to leave the boat at this stop.

He had brought his children to an island in this great broad stretch of river which he had often visited as a child. Then he had sailed to it most weekends during the school holidays, in a small dingy with his father. Once they had borrowed a larger boat and sailed down the river on a Friday evening in summer, anchoring a short distance off the island and spending the night on the boat; then they had landed very early the next morning, several hours in advance of any other visitors.

Hadn't his sister come with them once? He wasn't sure, he couldn't remember.

He looked back along the wide expanse of silky, gleaming water, back towards the city from which they had come; only two or three miles away it lay separated from them now by river and lake and forest.

With a slight shudder the boat drew perfectly alongside the quay. The boatman stepped off and secured the rope then turned to help the three of them as they stepped over onto the suddenly unmoving ground of the island.

They looked around them. A little way over to their left was another landing stage; a small, flat-bottomed ferry, just big enough to take a car and, milling around it, two dozen or so passengers, was making its way across the fifty metres of water which separated the island from the river's mainland bank.

He decided to strike out on their walk before the ferry landed and disgorged its load of day-trippers. But immediately he was surprised, looking about him, to find that he did not automatically know which way to go, did not, in fact, recognise the island at all. He had assumed that he would know exactly where to go – how to lead the girls on the best route around the island, taking in the little golden-yellow schloss, the pretty walled rose garden, the fountains and hidden grottos, the lawns where the peacocks were to be found, nonchalantly wandering. All these he remembered well. But now, as he stood looking about him, he was quite lost as to which direction to take, was surprised to see that no less than four routes – two of which, indeed, could be described as constituting actual roads, something he certainly did not remember of the quiet, protected island – seemed to offer themselves.

The two girls stood looking at him questioningly. Aware that the flat-bottomed ferry with its load of tourists must dock at any moment and immediately let down its front onto the slope of the nearby ramp, he settled, with an unconvincing impersonation of confidence, on one of the four available routes and the little party headed off.

But after only a minute or two he could feel the absence of cohesion in the little group just as much as he felt it between himself and his surroundings. He knew his lack of conviction – he was still, as they walked, looking for landmarks, for anything that would make him feel at home, make him feel, as it were, once more within his memory instead of so disconcertingly outside it – was communicating itself to the two girls; the more disconcertingly adrift he felt the more he tried to give them a feeling of security, and the more unreal everything came to seem.

They had taken one of the roads. There were no cars, no other walkers, despite the incongruous, well-maintained pavements, and on either side was dark forest – not ancient and green like the trees he remembered from the island but new, dark, and perfectly silent. This was nowhere anyone would walk simply for pleasure and soon the older girl said so, objecting.

And now they were all hungry, and it was already past time for lunch, which they had delayed until reaching the island, and their surroundings were almost as unlike what he had pictured for their picnic as it was possible to be, and it felt just as pointless to go on as it would have felt to stop or turn back, there on that smooth quiet road in the middle of a dead forest which blocked the sun.

Then, after only five or ten minutes, though certainly it felt much longer, they reached, of all things, a bus stop and he realised at last that something was wrong. It was a few moments more until, scrutinising the timetable fixed to the metal pole and translating as best he could the names of the stops, something which felt very strange occurred to him. Gradually, indistinctly, it dawned in him that they had disembarked not onto the island itself but onto the mainland bank opposite the island, and that the little flat-bottomed ferry was there to take them over that last short stretch of water to their destination.

Though he didn't find it funny – rather he was already clutching at the possibility with a sort of desperation of hope and relief – he told the girls what he thought had happened and tried to laugh and make a joke out of it. He told them they had actually been walking back towards the city.

But now the two girls were tired, it wasn't funny, and they were wondering what was so great about this island they were supposed to be going to anyway.

But when they turned around and walked back to the little landing station and all decided to buy ice creams while they waited for the little ferry to reach them – it was coming towards them already again, there was just enough time to choose the ice creams, lift the small card discs from their tops, unwind the paper covers and drop them into the basket and then run to join the small crowd as everyone stepped onto the lowered metal plate of the ferry which ground and clanked on the concrete ramp beneath – then quite suddenly they were grinning at each other and licking their ice creams and laughing at the sudden squash of people, squinting in the sunshine and looking over at the deep green of the island with interest and quiet, happy anticipation.

The small crowd of teenagers had somehow found its way onto the ferry also but now, standing somewhere towards the rear of the little community as it travelled over the few yards of water toward the island, seemed to have lost its allure in the sun and open air; rather he noticed his daughters watching a tall, tanned woman, brown and lean like a leather strap and carrying a small canvas knapsack on her back, as she stood beside the rail of the ferry and looked steadily at the island and then down the long stretch of river to where it curved and disappeared in the glittering city; she had the steady and purposeful air of one whose own feet would carry her wherever she wished to go, and though her knapsack was not tightly packed it was easy to imagine that it contained little less than the total of her possessions; she smiled faintly beneath the admiring looks of the two young girls, who exchanged quick glances with each other, eyebrows raised.

The ferry docked and a dusty rain of happy feet tramped once more onto solid ground; the woman like a leather strap struck off ahead while he and his daughters joined a young couple with a baby in a sling as they stood before a tall wooden signpost; at its top a number of narrow, arrow-shaped slats of wood, each carrying a word or two in the old gothic script, pointed off in this direction and that, clearly indicating the way to each of the island's features.

It was the peacocks the girls were eager to see, he knew that, and in this he was with them; wasn't it after all the peacocks, the almost incredible abundance of exotic, wandering peacocks, that had encapsulated and so profligately displayed to him the almost exuberant magic of the island on those visits of his childhood?

No sign mentioned them, but somehow a direction made itself felt to the party and soon they were walking happily along together, the various groups from the ferry thinning and dispersing around them to one direction or another.

'What's a *schloss*, Daddy?' asked the younger girl, and she bumped him gently as they walked.

'It's a castle or a fine house,' he said, 'like a manor,' and he bumped her back, a little harder.

'Mind yer manners!' she laughed, and then playfully she made a sudden lunge at him and quickly he reached out and pulled a tall grass from beside the path and turned and swished her with it, swishing both girls now as they laughed and ran from him to pull grasses of their own.

'Mind yer manners, mind yer manners!' they called to each other, swishing away at legs and bare arms while running unsteadily backwards away from each other, watching one another grinningly and guarding themselves half-heartedly while taking care not to move too far out of range. 'Swish! Swish!' went the grasses, before breaking their stalks and hanging down towards the ground, 'Swish! Swish!'

Now he darted forward and grabbed the little one about the waist and hoisted her up above him. She hadn't been picked up like that in a long time, she was too old for being tossed in the air; outraged and hysterical with laughter, lying horizontally in the air above his face, she screamed and squealed and hardly dared struggle in case he drop her. He smiled into her eyes as she shouted and laughed, beside herself with anger and glee. 'Put me down! Put me down this minute!' she demanded, but was overcome immediately with laughter at her own imperiousness, helpless and high above him.

But somehow only a few moments later all three were once more walking soundlessly, the girls on either side of him but none of them holding hands, and all he was aware of was the spaces between them and the returning absence of the peacocks. Where were they? But he did not want to mention it, though they all thought of it.

He looked around him. They had come to an area of wide, heathy lawns, nothing like the rich, sunny swards he remembered, and his mind struggled to populate them with strolling peacocks and the sudden, electrifying shiver and rustle of a tail being raised and then spreading itself. But there were no peacocks, there were not even any people, and he could only wonder at this desertion. Where was everybody from the little flat-bottomed ferry? Where had they gone to? He had not chosen particularly obscure-looking paths, had not sought deliberately to separate their party from the other groups of walkers and tourists. But now they were nowhere again, on the island or off it, and it was as much as he could do to feel the ground beneath his feet.

He asked the children if they were hungry but the words sounded irrelevant almost while he was still speaking them; the older girl shrugged her shoulders.

'I'm a bit hungry,' said the younger. He turned to her, lovingly grateful for this tiny and unselfconscious injection of energy. She looked up at him briefly then over towards her sister, who walked on dully, her head bowed.

He looked around for a suitable place where they

could sit and eat the sandwiches they had prepared that morning. There was nowhere particularly attractive, no spot that recommended itself more than any quite arbitrary other.

'We'll walk on a bit and stop at the next nice spot we come to,' he said. And with these words they returned again to just the place of feeling they had occupied before he had spoken.

His sister was two-and-a-half years younger than him. That's not much, he thought to himself, two-and-a-half years isn't much between a brother and sister. But I don't know her. Why don't I know her?

'When are we going to get to the peacocks?'

'I don't know,' he said, 'I don't understand. There used to be peacocks everywhere, they were just wandering all over the place, and in the mornings and evenings you could hear them screeching high up in the trees. They were everywhere.'

'Someone in my class brought a peacock feather back from Spain,' said the little one, 'But my teacher says it's bad luck to have a peacock feather in your house.'

'With some people, you know, that's the only thing they ever say about peacocks. You mention peacocks, or you're looking at a feather and how beautiful it is, and all they can say – and you just know it's all they're going to say – is *it's supposed to be bad luck to have a peacock feather in your house, you know.*'

'A child wouldn't say that,' said the older girl.

'No,' he said, 'you're right, a child wouldn't say that.'

'Why is it, anyway? Why is it supposed to be bad luck?' asked the little one.

'Heaven knows,' he said.

'Probably just because people who kept peacocks didn't want people stealing their tail feathers so they went around saying it was bad luck to have them. That's what I think anyway,' said the older girl.

'Quite likely,' he said. 'I know one thing. I never in all my life heard of one piece of bad luck that happened to anyone who had a peacock feather.'

'Well it's not like you see them in everyone's house anyway, is it?' said the older girl sourly. Now she was fed up with talking about peacocks. She wouldn't mind seeing some, she'd seen two in the garden of a country pub once and she thought they were cool, but she was fed up with talking about them. And she was hungry.

A little way up ahead the open area they had been walking through narrowed and the path turned to one side. Perhaps things would look different, he thought, the other side of the bend. But instead they found themselves walking through a patch of scrubby, ill-kept woodland. Over to their right they could see, through the bushes and thin trees, a number of what looked like wire pens with small coops inside. He suggested that they go over to take a look but the girls weren't interested; he went anyway.

It was unpleasant picking his way through the tall nettles and fallen branches. And when he got there there was nothing to see, only rusted pens and dilapidated coops. They reminded him of the pens for raising pheasant chicks which he had seen once on a relative's farm where shooting was the main activity.

When he turned around he saw his daughters standing over on the path some way away. He was surprised by how far he was from them, he had not thought he had come so far into the wood. They stood watching him. He waved to them, stood looking at them for a moment and then began to walk back.

'Perhaps they raised the baby peacocks there,' he said when he reached the girls. 'But it looked as if it hadn't been used for a long time.'

In another moment or two the path led out of the woody area and they saw a little way ahead of them the back of the yellow schloss. When they reached it they walked round to the front and sat in a patch of sunlight on the shallow steps of one of the two attractively curved arms of steps which swept down from its entrance. Looking out onto lawns and a dehydrated fountain they ate their apples and sandwiches and drank tea from a flask. When he looked at his watch he was shocked to find that it was nearly three o'clock.

Afterwards they went and sat on the grass in the sun.

'The way we used to get peacock feathers when I was a boy was to creep up behind one of them and then step on the tip of its tail, and the bird would run off and you'd be left with a feather under your foot!' He told them this with an air of what he had thought would be boyish mischievousness, thinking of it as a clever and amusing trick. But neither girl liked the story. They thought it was cruel.

'Daisy, d'you remember that thing Sarah was telling us about at school? Shall we try it?' said the older girl, addressing her sister.

'You mean the spinning thing?'

'Yes, shall we try it?'

'OK.'

'OK Daddy so what you have to do is, we all stand in

a circle, but quite wide apart, and you lift your arms up and put them out straight like this – out straight to either side – and then you turn quite slowly but getting a bit faster, just ten times to begin with, each person turning round on the spot with their arms out wide.'

'OK', he said, getting up from where he had been watching the older girl demonstrate what she meant. 'Is something supposed to happen?'

'She didn't say what's supposed to happen, she just said someone had shown it to her. You don't have to do it with other people, you can just do it on your own but if you do it together it's best to do it in a circle. She just said it's really good. But you're supposed to do it after some other exercises only I don't know those.'

'Do we take it in turns or all go together?' he asked.

'All together,' she said.

They positioned themselves so each had enough room to spread their arms and spin and then, each looking at the other for a moment, they began.

He moved slowly at first but was quickly surprised by how comfortable and balanced he felt, like something tall and slim and fine spinning freely and securely on a small but well-defined spot. On the second and third turns he realised that without trying to he was speeding up. The landscape around him began to blur and then, quite suddenly, the greens and browns and flashing yellow of the schloss changed to streaming emerald and peacock blue and he saw himself surrounded amid the swirling colour by ten thousand bright unblinking eyes. He was aware of his body continuing to spin but the radiant eyes remained motionless before him and then, in the dry, unvarnished tones of truth, they began to speak to him of his past. He saw himself and his sister as children, arguing viciously, and heard his mother's voice warning his sister 'Be careful. He's ruthless.' Then an overwhelming sense of having committed a crime with regard to his sister and a sudden lurch in his spinning while there rang in his ears the words 'But something had shut down, something had shut down.' He felt himself like a stone, like a starving child; like a spring blocked, fouling. But now his sense of spinning overcame him once again and then, joyously, everything began to flow; the eyes sank back into the blues and greens and

Bump!

He was sprawling over the grass, his head spinning and his older daughter lying half on top of him, laughing and rolling and heaving with breath, and he could only lie there and wait for himself and the crazy world to subside. But at some point had come into his mind, and into his chest and arms, the memory of once having taken his three-year-old sister in his arms, into these arms, to give her comfort and security, to protect her, at a time when they both had been alone and afraid. He had felt older than her, he had wanted and felt able to protect her, and he had acted out of that feeling and could feel it still, now, in his arms and in his chest. There had been one such time, he had felt the desire and ability to protect her and he had done so. And with this memory there came absolution.

Laughing and sprawling, father and daughter had begun hugging each other. Through laughter and heaving breath she was shouting something into his ear, but it was so loud and everything was still spinning so fast that he could not hear her.

'I saw the peacocks!! I saw the peacocks!!' she was shouting. 'They were *so friendly*!'

She was hugging him tightly as they rolled now, laughing and rolling over the grass. 'Daddy they were so *friendly*!' She seemed so grateful, so full of thankfulness to him! What was she thanking him for?

But it didn't matter, what did it matter, he didn't need to know anything; overcome with love, he hugged her back.

For some moments they lay together, still panting, and felt the coarse grass prickling their faces and wrists.

Sitting up he looked over towards Daisy. She was lying a short distance away, flat on her tummy with her face towards him. Her eyes were closed and she was breathing deeply and evenly; a contented smile shone from her.

'Daisy,' he called, 'Are you OK?'

'Mmmm,' she murmered, still smiling, eyes closed. She stretched out her arms further to either side of her and wriggled, slightly, a little deeper into the grass.

'What happened, Daisy? How did it feel?'

Her smile broadened but she didn't answer. He sat looking at her for some moments and then, he didn't know why, he found himself laughing. He wanted to run. Standing, he turned and asked the older girl if she wanted to race.

'OK, first to that tree over there.'

She jumped up and set off straight away, leaving him standing.

The girls were sharing a mattress on the floor. He was lying between them with the book of children's stories held open high above his face, reading aloud to the three of them. The

Fillyjonk was in a foul temper and they were all excited to learn what would happen next.

After finishing the story he put the book down on the floor and turned out the light, leaving only the light of the candle in its tin lantern. Nobody was sleepy.

'Daisy,' said the older girl.

'Yes,' her sister replied.

'What happened to you this afternoon, when we were playing spinning? Did anything happen?'

Daisy began to laugh. 'I'm not going to tell you,' she said.

'Oh come on,' said her sister, 'come on.'

'I'll tell you in the morning'.

'Promise?'

'Promise.'

But when he was kissing her goodnight she whispered to him. 'When I was spinning, Daddy . . . I was spinning with the whole earth, we were spinning together! And we love each other!'

'What do you mean?' he whispered back.

'Me and the earth,' she said, 'we love each other!' And she leant back then and looked at him.

Jeton Kulinxha

The Kosovar Peg

I turned to nothing to see nothing. Surmounting ideas on my forehead as if to say I had the audacity or the force to say No to the very ideas that mount my head, with assumptions that there is a mind, hence a brain to accommodate them all, a brain to say that there *is* something. Ideas and thoughts that were never mine. How could I in the end forgive myself for being so vulnerable? To say that my own mind doubted its own mind. Its intellect. Its existence. Bollocks! It could I suppose, for my very own lack of it, surprised by the very notion, have thrown the towel in and given way to aggravation of the most insensitive kind, and given authority to those buoyant ideas that common minds do create: the hideous self-doubt and loathing.

I cared not for the medals of the world and those pedestals or the fact that those ideas or medals may have helped the limbs move further. The ordinary mind within me made me stay closer to myself and to the tragedy of that proximity. Fair and square are the wicked and the noble for attempting to banish all that is true and painful. But I was never the one or the other and had no interest or the spirit to deny or accept either of the two.

Instead I let myself spiral down into the flow of time, thinking that all is fine and comprehensible. By the power of nothing did I seem vaguely spirited or to the idea affiliated. It just felt so; the calm vagrancy of an evaluating kind. The storms had bypassed me and I was there just as a buffer to the introspective thought. How foolish. How naïve. How yesterday. Nevertheless, I did not intend to break through an avalanche of philosophical ideas on how to better myself, nor indeed justify my very exposition of thought to the ponderings of my own mind. I chose, freely. Or so I thought, I believed.

I hang daily on a rope, regardless. I have my own hate and my own strength. And it is so fine. It is so fine I am accustomed to the tangible finesse of it all. Perhaps not too often do I hear it, but I do maintain the composure of that which is fine. To tell you the truth I have no inclination to speak that often. The very fact that I do not have a voice does not permit me to spread myself too often in a literary way and expose myself as a 'someone' who might have any-thing to say. I serve a purpose. That is, to cling to a rope and never let go. I am pressed, sure, and when they let go I do cling on harder. If that very mind of a mind did not mind I would let go and with a single freefall I would taste the grass and the dust, without consequences; without shame and without prejudice.

But, there was a fire on tonight, however. Across the fence. It made me realise that the person standing there wallowing in his own pitiful existence had assumed that there was a rainfall and he rushed out to see if all that tobacco of his was intact, whether his half empty glass of wine was saturated by heavenly juice falling foul from clouds. No, even the monotone solemn running drip from the drainpipe was not what he had imagined it to be at the moment, when his parallel world-view created an allegiance and everything just simply went wrong for him. Just to spite him, he thought. No, his expectations are not mistaken. He is just wrong. He is so wrong. *He* is wrong.

The man bypassed me and went over to where the

next door neighbour's fire had warmed up the fence and he leaned on it just so he could see how close he was to movement, to destruction, to things that are vigorous. To heat. To life. He had found himself dead on his feet when it dawned on him that even the boring mundane back garden fire over the fence was more playful, more lively, more cheerful than he could ever be. The liberty. The joy of it all, pinned him to the ground as he stared at the fire butterflies dance up in the dark blue sky, and even though for a finite moment in time, as they enjoyed their short-lived glory, they did it with more intensity and joy than he could ever imagine centuries on end would bring for him. He broke down in front of that fence. With shame he turned his back to it forever and all he could hear was the slow running drip of water from the roof that began to fall and crumble even merrier now. The security light of the common suburban paranoia lit up just in time. Exposed to the light of his own reflection and embarrassement, there was no sky small enough where he could hide. Conspiring against him, he thought, was not just the world, but the world he did not know too. How sad, how painful. Called himself a man not long ago, in front of witnesses.

That was the first time I wanted to trade places with him. To see how his alleged freedom worked. When all of my power held me against my will to a rope, all of his will had no power to stop the rope to his neck. The resentment I feel would have snapped that neck in two, more spectacularly than anyone could have ever contrived it. Long before the years lingered on and were wasted on him.

Still, the power of my own hatred keeps me hanging here. Until I'm pressed further, I'll keep watch.

Quiet desperation dawns

It's despicable; that *'old spot knowledge'*. That air of quiet confidence and overpowering wisdom. Where you know, and the more you know, the hunger and greed are greater. One wants to know and of course has to, and then whimsically brushes aside the ignorance that secretly resides within. It is difficult to grasp how vast the universe of knowledge really is. Then, one understands, with luck, and that is when bitterness sets in. In full force; greater than disillusionment. That is when hope is lost, when you finally accept that you know a lot about wrong but know too little to heal, but worse, the will; it's just not there.

Despair overwhelms your thoughts. There is a finite ability to expand further, anymore. There is something very sinister and decapitating in that revelation. You realise that it is too late to go back to the plain *'old self'* and youth; where everything is so simple and meek and forgiving. Baffled, you take notice of the passage of time. It's quite an unreal sensation. Like a finger clap that was never there or you were deaf.

Too fast perhaps? You counted the sheep by their legs and divided them by four.

The sense of closeness vanishes into dull thick air of overcrowdedness. Proximity changes heading as you desperately cling to the centre. Relationships crumble as if they were castles made of *Rizla* in a wet gloomy November dusk on a foreign shore. You stare and listen to a stream of words as if they were alien, something indistinct, something you have never, ever heard before. You try to understand while panicking and clenching your sweaty palms. Cold shivers shoot down your backbone and you fear war and love of anything, anyone, and yourself. There is no sound. There is no help.

A fresh thought slips your mind like a drop of olive oil would down the back of a spoon. A trace remains and that's when they spot you; just then, when your eyes give away that spark of credible sanity, long forgotten by all that it existed once.

You want to share, to give, to help, if only with words. They ask you and at first they don't understand; neither answers nor their own questions. You circle and hover with revelations, waiting for them to raise their eyebrows and smile, content that the puzzle is solved and mystery transforms into a useless rite. Sometimes they do and sometimes they don't. But you dart the bull's eye with first strike and they come back for more answers which become more complex and sensitive. In the process you find a few jovial facts about yourself that you had misplaced while too busy pretending to be looking for the truth and acting smug and pretentious. You touch down back to earth and with that single free fall, you find and recover some emotions you thought long gone; permanently erased. Breakpoint comes when they ask questions about themselves and you, and they know you know the truth of. How can you? How dare they?

They do and you can, but you don't. You lie to forgive them the faults and spare them the guilt they are ridden with by otherworldly bullets. You lie to cover the wounds caused by other lies. You become a brief monument of lies, and they sense it somehow; from your distant voice, from your anguish. Credibility dissolves like steam in clouds. They would rather be stabbed with honesty they do not know the meaning of. Just so they can taste that blood of viciousness and then deny wholeheartedly and unanimously while all along anonymous to you and themselves. A vision of clarity that you find too cruel to face them with erupts. They think of you as evil, as false. The master of deception unmasked, finally. They become taller than you for their own sake. Instant growth for the inferior thinkers, however short-lived. Hate, hung out to dry in the mist of their tears, plays all like puppets. You remove yourself with a slow broken walk and a bent back. You could have not been a saint.

You were unsure often, but never a saint. You kept yourself away from harm and the rest of the commodities associated with it. Never was there a time when you consciously embraced a good deed or an act of healthy will. It came naturally, unconsciously, without proper agreement or recognition of value. It came as normal, too common to mention. Too proud to advertise amongst enemies and friends, or subordinates and heroes, you regret, semi-remorsefully, and wish you could amend things through time without special attention to chronological order.

You regret failing to try to change people and your-self around them. You walked when you could have been running. You ran when you could have stayed indoors. You remember that hideous smell of burnt processed sausage, when you could have had an apple pie brought to you by a farm girl with rosy cheeks and a pure heart.

Consolation does not come. You drove it away in the wrong direction when you were strong, and now you are too weak to beg. Right and wrong become one at last, and you find yourself in the corner, old and lonely. You could only wish it is loneliness while you slowly die before you've lived. That is what you've refused to know all this time. Before you die.

Shelter

We were out this Thursday, Josh and I. Oh man what a night. I wasn't used to this kind of fun. No Sir, not at all.

I remember when I was a teenager. Yeah, this is what it reminded me of; when I was a teenager. We were all so not responsible for anything; irresponsible even. Gosh. They don't say 'gosh' anymore, but I remember, me and my friends used to. I still do though, but that is only when I get excited and something extraordinary happens. Yeah, 'gosh'.

My mate Josh used to get a lot of teasing about that because, well, we used to say Gosh-Josh for everything. I think it annoyed him sometimes, well most of the time but we didn't do it too often you see, and every time we did it, it was when we were having fun. So no, we didn't annoy him too much, no. Not that we were not having fun, it's just that we, kind of used it for extra fun times; like when my other mate Dan got a date for the first time with Amy. We were so happy then and we said 'gosh', without the 'Josh' though of course, but with relish. Josh mentioned that we should say Dan-Gosh, and we tried straight away, but no, it didn't sound as funny as we thought it did with Gosh-Josh.

Yeah, so Dan got a date with Amy and we were all so happy then. Yeah. I think Josh decided not to pursue the Dan-Gosh thing because well, he told me afterwards it would make it sound as if Josh wanted to be like Dan or the other way around, which it did. But he thought that we might think he doesn't like it when we say Gosh-Josh. Which he did, because he told me, it's just that he felt embarrassed and he did not want that much attention. We gave him a lot of attention though because he deserved more attention then we did. Josh was the chairman of the Maths Club and he was the leader of the Debating Club we went to on Sunday afternoons and he was always smart our Josh. Yeah. Plus Josh told me he fancied Amy too, which was not unnatural, because, well, because umm, well we liked Amy a lot. Well, maybe we all fancied her a lot because, well because she was very pretty, and smart, yeah she was very smart then, very smart. Pretty smart I say, but she didn't like Dan very much though, because she said he was boring and stupid. She didn't say it to Dan of course, well; *we* had to say it on her behalf. So after that Dan was heartbroken. He didn't go out with us for a month, he was so embarrassed.

So then Josh could not ask Amy out because he felt bad because of Dan, plus Dan was always with us in the Maths Club and debates on Sundays and all, that is; he came after the month long absence. So no, Josh couldn't ask her out. He was afraid too. Yeah, he was very afraid that Amy might find him boring and stupid too. He once said 'No! What if she…what if she thinks I'm stupid and boring?' We didn't think he was boring or stupid. Dan asked us if he was boring or stupid. We said no.

Josh looked at me and I was wondering if Josh wanted to ask the same question. But I don't think so.

'I think Dan was stupid' Josh says suddenly.

'Why?'

'Come on, he was as thick as a brick, his good looks were his saving grace and even then he would open his fat fucking mouth and that fucking thing with the nose job after the accident and shit.'

'Yeah.'

I looked at Josh this Thursday night and I thought he had changed a lot. Never saw him since high school. I went to college in our town. He moved abroad with his family. I never knew he was in London until he sent me an e-mail saying *Hi I'm in London. Fancy a pint mate. Josh*

Yeah, Josh had changed. He was very handsome though. I could see the girls at the club giving him the smiles and everything. Yeah he was very cool. He worked for a big bank and all. Dressed very trendy or so it seemed. I didn't care much about fashion and all, you know. When I asked him about the clothes he told me everybody will be trying to wear something like that soon. Yeah I believed him. He is so smart Josh. I missed Dan though. He was a very nice guy Dan. Very handsome. Every time I saw Josh, he reminded me of Dan.

Ah well...oh and then there was that party that summer before we graduated that Dan's older brother had, and we kind of sneaked in, because Josh said it would be fine. Dan's brother was in a room with a girl so we were safe. But then Josh tripped over something on the balcony and pushed the girl Dan was talking to, and then she fell on Dan and she looked a bit like Amy and I think Josh liked her most, but then, Dan was sitting on the edge of the balcony and the girl, I cannot remember her name, no; Nora, that was her name, Nora, she fell on Dan and Dan fell off the balcony.

He was badly hurt Dan. His parents came from their weekend at their cottage and they were very upset and they blamed Dan's brother for being irresponsible. Josh felt bad too and told me he could not forgive himself for being so clumsy and falling on Nora like that. Dan had that operation where the good doctors in our town put his nose together and stuff, but his face never looked the same again. I thought him handsome still but Josh didn't think so. Not like before. I think Nora liked him the most, maybe out of guilt for pushing him off the balcony or perhaps she could only see him the way she remembered him before the accident. Anyway, they got married, I think, and I heard that Nora had a lot of affairs with other men but Dan didn't mind. That's what they were saying anyway. Maybe Dan had affairs too, I don't know. These things are never certain.

'So how's life?' Josh yawns as he orders drinks.

'Yeah, it's good.'

'So you work for a…what do you do?'

'I am project manager for the foundation I told you.'

'Right,' he says, still yawning.

Josh could not remember a lot of things I told him this Thursday. I guess he had a lot of things to think about. But also, he was mostly busy checking out the ladies that went by our table.

We danced a bit earlier. I am not a great dancer but Josh found us a table in this club and our table was right in front of the floor where everybody danced. So we mostly looked at other people dancing. I didn't go out on Thursdays. My day was Friday after work for a couple of hours, or then maybe Saturday late lunch or early dinner you know, with friends or something. But everybody stayed late on weekends and I usually rented a video or watched telly or read a book. Once I stayed so late on Saturday at a neighbour's party and I woke up too late and missed *'Sorry I haven't a clue'* on Radio 4.

'Do you have a girlfriend?' Josh asks.

'Um, no I don't, I, I don't have, no I don't have a girlfriend, no.'

'Do you see those two girls behind you?'

I turned around slowly and saw the most beautiful creatures I had ever seen. I never actually saw anything like that before. Maybe those girls on TV, or you know those girls in magazines, but much, much prettier. I almost said 'gosh', but then I realised that Josh had hated that word ever since Dan's accident or so. He told me never to say 'gosh' again and especially not 'Gosh-Josh'. He had said it so seriously it scared me a bit. But I was fine, I could not say 'gosh' I accepted, at least when Josh was around. Once I almost said it and only the G— came out and it sounded more like G—ow.

Josh had squeezed my arm so hard that my eyes and his almost popped out. Never again.

I didn't say 'gosh'. I looked at the girls and turned around at Josh and I said wow.

Josh stared at me for a while, then smiled and told me I could say 'gosh'.

'Really?'

'No, not really, you're a grown man for Fuck's sake'

I really, for a moment, I really felt good about saying 'gosh' and I thought about what would've happened if I did.

'Don't you think the one on the left looks a bit like Amy?'

I looked at the girls and they were both beautiful, but the one on the left she did look slightly like Amy, although I didn't know how Amy looked since we were sixteen.

Amy disappeared when we were kids. No one knew where she went or why or how. Her dad came three days after the news broke out. He was away on business, overseas, in Japan, for a whole month and they had trouble contacting him and her poor mother was running on the streets asking everybody if they had seen her Amy. She cried and begged and screamed and pleaded and we all felt guilty and useless that we could not help or do anything. We were frozen. The town froze. We were frozen. We were.

Then Amy's dad came. A big man. We hid. No one could look him in the eye. First he calmly walked around and went about, confident he would find her. Then, with every passing day he slowed down then stopped. He was defeated. Life defeated him, the great man he was. Another's life defeated him. I had never imagined such a great man to crumble like that. In a short time he grew thin and pale.

Amy's mother she turned grey. She was found in the woods outside town. She took a lot of tablets and held a photograph of Amy in her hand and slept forever. Amy's dad moved away because he could not bear to stay in town anymore. Amy was their only child, and with Amy's mother gone too, I guess he wanted to, you know, forget, or maybe escape, I don't know. We avoided passing by their house. As if, I don't know, it just didn't seem right walking by, you know, with everything and all. It made you sad. We were sad. I cried a lot afterwards. I liked Amy a lot. And her parents. They were nice. I remember Amy's mother cooking biscuits for school days out. I wanted my mother to cook like that. I never knew my mother. Sometimes I even wished Amy's mother was my mother.

Josh had seen Amy the day before. I guess he saw

her more often that last month before she disappeared but he told me not to say anything to anyone because of Dan. But Dan had only gone on one date with her and that was a long time ago. Still, Josh said Dan still loved her and he would get upset if he knew Josh was making friends with her. So I didn't say anything to anyone. I didn't want word to spread around and hurt Dan. I was in a way wishing I could see Amy but Josh was, you know, making friends with her, so I thought, you know, Josh is cool and maybe Amy will think I am boring. So no, I thought Josh would be best for her. Maybe through Josh I could, you know, say hi to her sometime. But she disappeared.

Josh showed me a letter later. In confidence. He told me that Amy had written it the night before she disappeared. It said: *You are evil and I don't want to ever see you again. Ever. Amy*

Josh told me that she wrote that the night before she disappeared and asked him to give it her parents. Josh was quite not himself for a long time after that. He asked me what I thought of the letter. I shrugged and tried to say something but I didn't. No, I said nothing. I guess he loved her a lot, like I did, like Dan, like everybody. But I guess he loved her more, Josh. Josh never gave the letter to her parents and made me swear never to tell anybody about it. I said OK.

I kept wondering why Amy thought her parents evil. But she was so happy and her dad was the greatest man in town, everybody loved him And her mother, a very pretty soft spoken lady, she was friendly with everyone. In the letter she never said *Dad, Mother, you're evil.* She only said *You are evil.* But I believed if that was what she said to Josh, then, I believed *him*, because he was my friend and he would not lie to me, plus he loved her, so yes, I really had no idea what to think.

I remember hiding behind a bush one day after Amy disappeared and I heard two police officers talking about Amy, in front of her house. They said that there are a lot of kids that disappear like that and they never find them, or they come back one day looking much older and tired.

The police officers thought someone had stolen her but they could not tell her parents that, unless they had proof. They had no proof. They mentioned Amy's parents. Nothing; just chit-chat and coffee, and crackling of radio. I felt they almost expected Amy to walk back home so they could stop her at her door and tell her off for worrying everyone and all that.

They had nothing. We were left with nothing. Amy had gone. Josh and his family left soon after that. It was as if something sucked the soul out of our town, out of us. Out of me.

'So what do you think?'

'Yeah, a bit. Amy was prettier though'

'Of course, but do you see it? The hair, the eyes.'

'Yeah, I see her.'

Josh kept staring at the girl. She must've been twenty, her friend younger. I could not turn around every time to look at her, so I thought of Amy. I saw her all the time. In my dreams, in car parks, the sky, the woods.

The girls came over to talk to Josh. They laughed a lot as if the universe depended on them laughing. I didn't like them much, but they were pretty. They asked me if I was shy. When I thought about it and tried to say no, Josh asked them to come with us to the bar of his hotel. They did. As we walked I tripped Josh the same way I had at the party when Dan had the accident. He almost fell over the girls. They thought me clumsy and shy and laughed even more. I felt nervous. The girl that looked like Amy made me nervous. It reminded me of that time when Josh and I saw Amy for the last time; that night before she disappeared. When we took her to the woods and left her alone inside the old cave by the stream.

On her own, lonely and cold.

Josh told me she wasn't there any more. She had gone travelling to Australia; then climbing Kilimanjaro; sailing across the world; teaching English in Nepal; writing poetry in the Gobi Desert; living with secret tribes along the Amazon; running free like a mustang with her long hair flying in the wind, leaping in the air in slow motion, with a great smile and sparkling eyes, like a star.

I doubt it.

The girls kept laughing, unaware.

A4 bedroom – An ode to a chicken

You are young and innocent
full of hopes and dreams
and wings to fly with
occasionally

We are old and greedy
full of fat and gluttony

and cars to drive in
often

The custom has it
we meet
briefly

And 40 odd days later
we part
amicably

Content and with a full stomach
we dream of dark fizzy drinks
and paper tissues
with names that twist

We meet again
in long alleys of goods
you are there modelling
frozen, as you do

We leave together
to the nearest kitchen
or barbeque

The news tell us
they raided your bedrooms
but never found you

Poesía de tipo tradicional
Anonymous poems from the oral tradition

translated from Spanish by Jim King

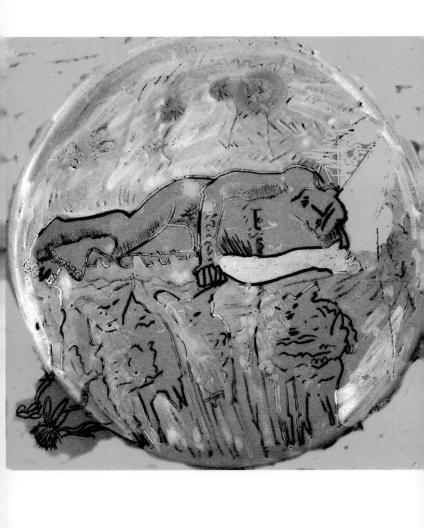

I went to the pool to fish,
but all I caught was stars
and leaves of the lemon tree.

Your body is an hourglass.
I hug your waist
to stop time passing.

I fell in love with a monk,
silently,
and in the twinkling of an eye,
the whole convent knew.

The beekeeper kissed me,
and the kiss tasted of honey.

Just because I kissed you, my love
my mother scolded me:
give me back the kiss I gave you.

I shall not gather vervain
early midsummer's day,
because my love is going away.

Picking olives –
so marriages are made,
who does not go to pick olives
will not fall in love

My eyes cannot sleep,
cannot sleep.
Mother, I was dreaming
three hours before daybreak –
the rose was flowering,
pine under cold water
Cannot sleep

I went to the sea for oranges,
but the sea had none.
I came out ringing wet
from the waves that come and go.

The galleys are leaving
the harbour, mother,
their sails taut,
wind at the stern.

To watch them rowing
I went up astern;
To the splash of the oars
I fell fast asleep.

River of Seville,
how beautiful you look;
white galleys,
green branches. (Lope de Vega)

The leaves are whispering,
mother, in the wind,
and their rustling is lulling me
to sleep in their shade.

Whispering breeze that blows
and delights in all things,
make music for me
in the leaves of the elm
while my love is sleeping.

My joys – almond blossom,
born early, then lost.

Because it sleeps alone,
Water wakes up frozen.

Say an *Our Father*
For Juan Fernández.
– Lord, is he dead then?
– No, I'm going to kill him.

In Avila, my eyes,
Inside Avila.
In Avila on the river,
They killed my love,
Inside Avila

Shining moon
bring light all night
Shining moon,
Silver, white
Shine all night
On my beautiful love.
Shining lover
Bring light all night.

Time and disillusionment
are two faithful friends
who wake the sleeper
and instruct the ignorant.

A man, to be a man,
Needs these three qualities,
Much do, little say,
No self praise his life long.

László Marsall

translated from Hungarian by Maria Schiller and Hilary Kassman

Kucorognom dívány ölében

Lazing on the Divan

Recently I've lost all appetite
for the war waged on white paper,
breaking in the winged horse,
schooling the bones of Pegasus.
Far better to slip from his saddle,
stretch out on the ground
watching wild, brindled rabbits.

Conjure me a vast divan
no matter how old and shabby
that I might sink within its depths,
a dish of pears and plums that drop
not to earth but in my mouth
and a bottle of Szürkebarát
to brighten my throat.

Let the parliamentary crows
caw in pyjamas
high above
beyond my bite.
I'd pull on old clothes
and doze
baking my belly in the sun.

With cars in the distance
growling out their hurly-burly,
I would light a small candle,
for now that is the minor-cosmic
lazy, idyllic,
flickering night I desire
simply, perfectly to be.

Primavera táncol az asztalomon

Primavera Dances On My Table

Heads down like sleeping bats, embryos are turning
towards spring, stirring in their mothers' wombs,
the ancients' 'waker-uppers'; but from behind my
                                        bookshelves
a grim gentleman cries 'oratio recta!'
Crows that still roost under parked cars
take off from mounds of fag-end pocked snow
to alight at dawn on your fur hat conferring
a crow-crown for your journey to work.
Yet in my imagination the blackbird polishes his rhetoric,
the tit, the most fearless of the forum in the trees,
perches on my elongating hand;
there's an old book in my library
where Cicero
champions them with a lengthy apologia.
But the books are frozen, once more we have snow.
And now the prolix old classicist exclaims
– Black the crow, white the snow –
'tertium non datur – in abstacto…'
I hurl a tit at him: 'Peck off his nose'
the library erupts, books split open
while the offended raven, a Primavera of sorts, dances on
                                        my table,
a tit is tangled in my hair and a blackbird tears my flesh.

255

Öregember karácsonya, 1989

Old Man's Christmas 1989

No golden walnuts or tinsel or fudge,
we only had them in the old days of peace.
But to me even the year before last was peace.
Now I shall tie a ribbon round its neck,
go down to the street,
the ever more deserted street,
and take my Christmas tree for a walk.
With luck it will bark at someone
or be given some crumbs of poppy seed cake for supper.
Perhaps it will drop a tiny Christmas tree,
and if I can sell the little love
with the money, maybe I could buy
a jar of plum jam.

I walked my Christmas tree.
Not an orphaned soul in sight.
Its thorn teeth bit my leg,
I slapped its backside
immediately it bit my palm.
Little rogue! You even have teeth in your arse?

You are neither man nor angel,
but the Devil himself!
Not an orphaned soul in sight
I hung my tree by its ribbon
on an ornate, glittering, old doorknocker.

Egy barokk kanálra

On a Baroque Spoon

And towards the end I found myself in a drawer,
in the diminishing family of precious metals;
then I lived at a pawnbroker's;
then at a red-nosed alcoholic's, a kind of receiver of stolen
goods.
After that – as they say, as a result of an advertisement – I
retired,
like an old army officer,
into a dark drawer, into the family of precious metals,
into a cold, black and unequivocal dreariness.

Sándor Weöres

translated from Hungarian by Maria Schiller and Hilary Kassman

Az Unicornis Látogatása

The Visit of the Unicorn

He prances in my room with delicate tread,
warily picks his way between heavy furniture,
my scattered clothes visible through his breastbone.
Slim blue hooves hover over the floor,

on his breath the embroidered flowers of my pillow.
His dark eyes rest softly upon me
he neither fears nor pities me,
his life and death a mystery.

Beside his step moonbeams
are crude as mud,
and the room is quick with desire.

Since disembodied rapture is seedless,
as he gazes, his innocent beauty languidly
glides into the moonlight.

Outer and Inner Space

Where the blue of morning
wriggles into the house,
they are busy at the gate of dreams,
one girl bathes in the brook
the other makes pancakes.
My mother cradles a bird and sets it free,
while deep under covers
I am still asleep,
the bird flies away
over the gate to the hills
and keeps going until
I am wide awake.

Estharang

Evening Bells

A shadow-tendril weaves into the landscape,
the red bull of the sky returns home.
He ambles down the slope in fiery mist,
rests on a gilt-edged cloud.

Dark hills recline as bullocks,
every tower a child sentry.
The mingled blood of small bells
spills onto the rooftops.

Here and there, stars come out.
Donkeys trudge to the far end of the village.
In the shadows of tall, slim poplars
a gypsy girl awaits her lover.

A fat water-beetle swims on the stream
he fashions lace in the foam from the evening glow.
The garden is still, not even a breeze,
the lazy dust lies in the road.
But in the forest an icy storm errupts,
builds a mountainous landscape in the clouds.
The faraway tempest sounds its battle cry
and tears into the headdress of the twilight.

Téli Csillag

Winter Star

Through a chink in the window
a star gazes at me
as though its frosty blade
wanted to slice
a confession from
my brain
or maybe my heart
of what good I have done
what wrong I have committed
what I have omitted
but I am silent
because I don't know
star-language
yet perhaps a spark
strikes from me
and the geysers
and volcanic ash
understand this
and from the window
the radiance
into a perhaps
reassuring perhaps
ominous blackness
fades slowly away

Évvég

Year's End

Bundled in heavy cloud,
winter leans over the forest.

Night after night then day
by day it wraps around.

It shrouds it at first
in fast melting snow,

but gradually white lace
smothers the trees.

It creeps along bare branches
the harvest weighing them down,

fattens on dark stumps
like a life force.

Distant mist petrifies under
the rush of an icy wind,

A faint ray of sun signals
it will all melt away in spring.

Útközben

Along the Way

I fill my glass with fiery night
knead my bread from cold mud;
distant light protects the one
who drinks the darkness of this world.

A Költő

The Poet

My life lies low, like a rabbit in the fields
turned by gun shots and wild animal hunger.
I live in my work, a winged tawny lion
that on your behalf will fight and never desert.

A Szegény Denevérek

The Poor Bats

The poor belfry bats
no one has taught them to count.
Though their worn skirts have holes
this is the least of their worries
since they can mend themselves.
But no one has taught them to count,
they know neither whole numbers nor fractions.
With a double-headed silver spoon
they stir curds
in a gold-rimmed cup
from the Veszprém coronation.
Then they notice that
there is neither spoon, nor cup, nor curds.
If they ask, what is the time?
here is a clock in the belfry before them,
but they can't read it,
since no one has taught them to count!

Eeva-Liisa Manner

translated from Finnish by Emily Jeremiah

Niin vaihtuivat vuoden ajat

So the seasons shifted

Spring, summer and autumn share the year. There isn't really a winter, only winter's sister, wan autumn. The day the rains fall, autumn has come from the North. The rain roars, it's as if the Madrid express train were hurtling past, endlessly long; at night, the distant rumble sounds, reminiscent of an earthquake. Matches fail to light, there is water under the glass face of my waterproof watch. A moth crawls on the wall, large and frightened like the face of a child.

  In the morning, when I look to the mountains, there aren't any. Emptiness has upset its cup, the mountains have disappeared, just as if a giant's hand had moved them over to Africa. There is no runway, either, only the abyss of the fogs. The pearl curtain of the rain covers my door, in front of the door is a threshold of scattered petals. The yard is domed and risen like bread.

Lumen kajoa eli ritarillinen kuolema
täysissä talonpojan varustuksissa

The Gleam of Snow
Or a chivalrous death in full peasant gear

It is evening, it is autumn. Is it also autumn where you are, or is it winter already, has your heart turned to winter? Are there tracks in the snow or is everything covered? Is the area newborn and fresh?

On the mountains, the gleam of snow, a black carriage travels in the snow, the horse has reached the far side of the mountain or disappeared into the dark evening. The simple cart, made by a country carpenter, it too vanishes now, I hear only the creaking. Now not even that, just the whisper of the wind in the olive trees.

It was just a reminder, an image, nothing solemn; rough wheels, no greeting from banners and ribbons, just the knocking of the wheel on the village road. It moves from the future in this direction, although it just went past.

A reflection that for a moment tied the laces of the universe, real for all that, my conveyance from afar, and the groom walks next to me, death has many grooms, the shrillthroated youth urges the humble horse on. It has come through the forests, it has the resin-scented wind in its mane.

Just the leap of the future into the present; but some day the omen and the bright image will unite on an autumn-dusky road; that day has been determined: the dizziness of death; and I ride in my carriage, idle, I lie in the hay, and the groom walks and goads, sorrow and song, earth's weariness, in his throat. We ride in the light of the snow, and the seasoned horse moves at an even trot, copper buckles in its harness, sounds in the buckles; it shakes music from its harness, like before.

Spekulaatio n:o 2

Speculation no. 2

Death has completed its manuscript, I skim it from day to day, I skim and I read from the end to the beginning, the leaves are already breaking, the leaves in front are still green but it's an illusion, only my eyes are green, only my eyes. The leaves have already been stripped from the tree of life, the veins are delicate and empty, the leaves translucent; are the frail, empty days of my life really there?

But one shouldn't begin a manuscript from the back or the front, the wise ones say; that which is behind is no longer; that which is ahead has not yet come. One should look only at this moment, which still quivers in the tree, green and lively, refracting light, itself mere light.

But it does not quiver, it twitched just now, I did not see it, this moment falls away, it falls away each moment and I do not see it falling, when I see it, it has already fallen. So it is with all moments, those gone, which are no longer alive, and those to come, which are not yet alive. The present is severance, but I do not see it.

This indicates that a philosophy of the present is impossible.

Motiivi numero 2 eli idean palautuminen

Motif number 2
Or the recurrence of an idea

In front of each deed I see an abyss over which I would have to jump. But every time I assess the gulf and the jump, and because I reflect, I do not jump.

I am myself that abyss. Would a jump therefore constitute victory over myself? No; I would simply be running ahead of myself; instead I have to lower myself, not jump. Each time I have to lower myself ever deeper into the unknown.

The meadows are on the other side, here the dark night of the soul. Lost jump! I want to take the shoes from my feet and wade in the deep grass, feel the warm earth and the cool grass against my soles. Sit in the grass, touch it, feel its fragile life, which has sprung from the earth's unconscious. Press my cheek against the grass, forget, sleep, fragments of dream around me. I wanted, I have wanted; why do I want no longer? Because the senses always want more; in the end I would like to be the grass myself.

So I choose an existence on this side, the inevitable modality of solitude, a very abstract existence, in which I would like only an existence without emotions, myself without conditions. The abyss of freedom.

Muistin vaunut

The Carriage of Memory

The snow covers the regions where battle has occurred. At the edge of the road, trees like drawings, behind them the frozen river. Southern trees and snow, covering the traces. Southern trees and spotted snow, a bird flies through the air, it has been hit and will freeze in a moment.

The black carriage departs without leaving tracks in the snow. There is a woman in the window who is being taken into the past. She is reading a book, she sits and moves, facing away from the direction of travel; she is herself the book. 'Fates have already been determined, no need to ask the soothsayers.' The line recurs, recurs, the book's or the bird's sentence, or just the fragile prediction of the buckles. Shots melt the river's covering, soon her body will swim in the river, the eyes' skin will cover the changing views.

The carriage is upside down on the road, springs come and go, the grass masks the conveyance with green. A tree grows through the broken shaft, the river flows silent and polishes its stones. The trees are immense. The river is a woman and sleeps. She is herself the river and changes the whole time from day's woman to night's woman;

now she is just Arno's whisper, the sound of water that has gone.

Uni

The Dream

I was walking alongside the graveyard wall when I noticed that I was being followed by a dark figure carrying a coffin on his shoulders. His load was as small as a trinket box, perhaps there was just an urn inside containing ash and brittle bones. Or perhaps the bearer was a shoeshiner with his black casket, they look like coffins. Then I realized that it was my shadow, Der Schatten. Myself, then, my shadow-me, my night, was accompanying me, pursuing me with its burdens around the town wall, which watches over its graves. A graveyard the size of a town. What else are towns like, if not whitewashed graves? Only the shoeshiners are alive, hungry and eager to attack shoes and make a bob. The town is a grave and a shoe, made of cement. The town is an enormous cement shoe, cementerio.

Hilary Kassman

Ephemera

L ondon. It has been said before but this time there is no
prelapsarian paradise waiting on the last page. My love
died at the foot of Nelson's Column. Died of starvation. I
lay helpless beside my beautiful Alphonse as he faded and
finally stretched stark. I had no food, any we had managed
to find he had always put into my mouth. There used to be
more than enough but we who live on and by the streets
have been deemed a menace and though they cannot cull us
directly, every other strategy of terror has been used to
eliminate us. Have you ever sat beside your beloved only to
see the light dwindle and look finally into a fixed, staring
eye? We live in the midst of plenty but every attempt we
made to eat was shadowed by a cruel wing of power. By the
time we decided to leave the area our families had lived in
for generations, Alphonse was too weak for the journey. He
collapsed in Trafalgar Square among the well-fed going to
look at the beauties of the National Gallery. Only, they were
blind to the beauty dying at their feet. Perhaps if I could
have put a great gold frame around him or mounted him on
a plinth they might have looked again; or at least not have
averted their eyes.

I gave a last look at his poor, sharp legs and decided
I should flee while I still had the strength. My only chance
for survival was to move away from this haunt of hunger. I
was scared of the parks; I knew murders happened there. I
used to have a friend who slept in St. James's before she was
killed. She told me how at night, she would see the keepers

removing eggs from the swans' nests. I wanted to fly from places where royal prestige was maintained by surreptitious cruelty.

We were not alone in suffering official destruction. My friends who frequented doorways on the Strand reported that the sleepers in their bags and boxes were nightly deliberately doused by the cleansing department's vans. Westminster Council's final solution to the problem of the homeless seemed to be literally to wash them away. Is civic hygiene always achieved through moral filth?

Alphonse used to say I looked like the woman with a siren's voice, the beauty of Helen and the courage of Achilles. I can't say how far I resembled Sinéad O'Connor but I know I wasn't feeling valiant. I hoped if I went up river to the edge of the city I might find a deserted loft, a crust and peace to grieve. My best chance of making the journey would be by water, given my depleted state. It was well past the equinox, so I thought I shouldn't have too much difficulty later that afternoon, in finding a dark corner on one of the river craft and sailing up to Richmond, without being detected.

Once on the boat there was plenty to eat. Boxes of half-eaten chips were strewn under the benches. A few children saw me as I darted from my hiding-place and threw part of their sandwiches in my direction. There were even pieces of fried chicken but I refrained from those, especially as they made me think of Alphonse.

Life in Richmond was tricky since it meant invading another's patch. However my timidity was a protection and eventually I was left alone. During the autumn and winter many of us succumbed to 'flu and died. Although I recovered, I was in a miserable state and kept noticing distressing sites, for example the displaced cormorants on the river, which I suppose must have been driven inland by lack of fish in the sea. They would stand holding out their shabby wings, waiting perhaps for a gust of salt air to be blown up river. I do believe that it was my state of mind which led to my being the catalyst, despite my dislike of cat words, for the murder.

One spring day, the river in spate, I had wandered a little along the towpath towards Kew. While I was pulling at some tender grass, I heard terrified squeaking and saw the desperate eyes of a group of tiny ducklings that must have been washed out of their nest and were being carried all together at a great rate along the water. The current was so fast, and in any case I can't swim, that there was nothing I could do. I remembered my mother telling me about the day a boy had rescued her when she had been thrown into a canal by a gang and felt sick at my inability to save the ducklings.

As I dragged myself along the sandy track searching for food, since hunger and the will to live are not logically related, I realised I was being followed by a fat, healthy, Home Counties type. He was clearly an overfed Surrey mummy's boy. Everything about him was glossy and complacent as he strutted after me. I drew into the grass at the side of the path thinking he might waddle past but he stopped and leered at me with his stupid eyes. There were two young fellows sitting on a bench nearby who seemed to find the situation entertainment for their personal pleasure. I scuttled on hoping my follower would retreat but he came alongside and introduced himself as Brandon. I wanted to know his name as little as I desired his attentions but he was impervious to this and considered his talking to me a great condescension.

Meanwhile the two young blades had strolled up to us. One of them had a Slav accent and the other lanky one sounded home-grown. The Slav kept comparing me with his lost love Natalia. He said I looked sad like her and that Brandon, although he didn't know his name, was pestering me in the way a dreadful character called Vladimir had pursued Natalia until she had jumped off a bridge to escape him and been drowned. Lanky legs said indeed, I resembled his own tragic love Natalie. His friend disputed that he had ever had such an affair until the quarrel became quite nasty. At that moment the Slav whipped out a gun and pointing it at the unsuspecting Brandon, who had continued parading around me in a grotesquely self-important manner, yelled, 'This is for you Vladimir,' and fired. Apart from the awful bang all I knew were a storm of feathers and a Slav voice shouting, 'Who wants to eat roast pigeon?'

Molly Dancing

All night it had rained but the morning was fair when we two brothers joined the other lads at the pithead on the end of the street, waiting for the miners who'd give us money. Standing each one of us in our sisters' dresses, were we vague, far flung descendants of Molly Maguires? To us, our May Day festivity meant a few pennies in the hand, nothing more; anyway dressing in our sisters' out-grown frocks was normal – we wore them at night, there being no money clothes. Once I rushed home from school for my team-issued football shorts, couldn't find them anywhere. Eventually Mam cried out in exasperation 'I'm wearing them'. There was a match; I had to have them, though they felt crusty.

End of April and it's raining. The world is drier than it was fifty years ago. My son is in the desert dressed in khaki, put on at seventeen knowing nothing, just money in the hand. Do we pass on more than our ignorance? What mumming awaits my grandsons? For whom will they stand waiting for pence? It's a'gate Molly dancing.

Theseus Sails from Dalston to Docklands

You are not his first Ariadne
there were others before
abandoned with their children

You thought
having stayed
almost thirty years
and growing a paunch
he had settled on the chair of forgetfulness

Today he has kicked it over
and with hair thinning
but thighs intact
set sail once more
to fulfil that hint of every son's mother
the divinity at least of half
the fathering

He seeks
within other female walls
to satisfy the final lust of age
be raised a god at board and bed

Let him though beware of heights
above that girded water

Scissors – Stone – Paper

for Kevin

At Tampere we were parted forever
after thirty years hooped
over middle finger and thumb

I shall never see the basalt you stooped
to pick up for me on your native shore
banned from your bag at Ballykelly

Paper remains
an uncut sheet to shroud
a lament for losses
bearing the cruel weight of words until
triumphed by tears
it disintegrates whichever way you play

Fleece dark grows the silence

Fleece dark grows the silence
the dead erupt like sandworms
drawing casts of their lives
on sleep's ebb tide

And outside in a rising wind
white sheets begin to struggle
as an old image of the soul
tearing from the body

Bedrock

An indefinable smell had invaded the house when I returned from school that afternoon. As usual I climbed the uneven steps to the bedroom to change my clothes. I opened the door – a dead soldier had been laid out on our high, white bed. Why had nobody arranged his hands? He opened his eyes, looked straight at me and closed them again. I felt my mother's palm over my mouth; she led me from the room.

We went up another flight of stairs to the attic. Here I often played as children like to do, performing their arcane rituals in places they imagine no one else remembers. The blue of the distant hills bloomed as though at the end of a tunnel, from that small windowset in thick walls, its deep ledge, cradle of my impulses.

Now the room looked ordinary with a small, make-shift bed and my clothes, removed from the dark chest of drawers, folded in a box. I asked my mother how long I would have to sleep here and she, surprised at my question, answered, 'Always, of course.' Anyway, my mother added when she saw my tears, I could not have continued sleeping with her, at seven I was no longer a baby. Although I was aware not another boy my age in the village still slept in his mother's bed, I had believed the beautiful child with her green eyes, whom she loved so, would be an exception. The war would never end, and my father remain forever in his wooden frame beside our bed. I wanted passionately to embrace her and I wanted to kill her. Had she shown any sorrow, I might have forgiven her, but by the implication that this was also for my good, she unwittingly taught me the delicacy of inflicting pain.

Over the years, the germ of farewell has stimulated each new conquest. Women do not refuse the mother's son who understands them so subtly. Above all, my wife in her solitude, supports and nurtures me, ever awaiting my return.

Descent

His head didn't need hair, smooth and brown as a banister end. Rings in his ears and, on a nimble finger, one wrought from a lump of gold he had dug out of the earth himself. Everything else he owned was in a tin trunk at his feet, apart from the African Grey that sat on his shoulder. Once he must have found a woman, impossible though to imagine his coming that close to another human being. The moment he arrived I recognised him. But when my mother said he was her father – she might as well have laid claim to Cinderella's silk slipper as one of her own shoes.

It was hot, the rest is lost. Wherever it was he went his parrot failed to accompany him. Over fifty years on, it's still living at the grocer's in the village. As I grow older my curiosity increases. When young, with such a deep horizon, what did it matter how he had landed in that light smelling of elderflowers or where he went later? I just wanted to keep turning the pages; Jack and the Bean Stalk, I'd never come down. Today when I would like to hold a page awhile, they blow over faster and faster.

So, whether I'm wanted in a dinner jacket or as Puss in Boots, I play, his ring on the same finger, my hands his.

Rain God

Mater Dolorosa

Shattered shoulder
almost blind
no legs
says
he is proud to receive this medal
from that dumpy
old woman in pink coat and hat

She stands gazing out by the chair from which
sprouts the trunk of her nineteen year old son

Private View

'I was born in Yalta'

glasses joggle red and gold cheeks
on the silver tray

'Before the Revolution
my father looked after the vines
they had survived for centuries
Peter the Great
the Russian Revolution

but under Stalin's prohibition
all were destroyed'

and the squat *Kremlin
Highlander* torrential swiller
of Georgian wine?

Angus Dubh / Agnus Dei

All the while his invective roared
his feet snuggled in woollen socks
knitted by his Mam

Danse Macabre

First day at school you danced on the tables

You would have enjoyed
gurning and jigging
to this skeleton music
but wouldn't have been able
to tuck away your bones
in the morning

The crematorium dealt with that

Solent Solstice

Blue-green gilded solstice sea
skimmed by evening pleasure craft
spread with the balm of money

At the town dump
bales of green silken grass
tumble away
as camels' milk
poured into the sand
in times of glut

while the open
spaces
between the bars of my rib
cage are filling
with the bones
of animals poking
through the engulfing desert

Twilight

Beyond raindrop shimmering glass
the cherry shines white in lilac
scented air
I put my hand on your head
slip down your neck
the meeting of skin and fur
a pledge
silent
secret
repeated
so long as rain falls

Edith Södergran

translated from Swedish by Jim King

Lyckokatt

Luck Cat

I have a luck cat in my embrace,
which spins threads of luck.
Luck cat, luck cat,
get me three things:
get me a golden ring,
to tell me I am lucky;
get me a looking glass,
to tell me I am lovely;
get me a fan,
to whisk away my weary thoughts.
Luck cat, luck cat,
spin me something else around my future.

En fången fågel

A Captive Bird

A bird was held captive in a gilded cage
in a white castle by a deep blue sea.
Langishing roses promised sensual delight and happiness.
And the bird sang about a little village high up in the
                                        mountains
where the sun is king and silence queen
and where a few little flowers in gleaming hues
bear witness to life which stubbornly endures.

Skogsdunkel

Forest Darkness

In the melancholy forest
there lives a sick god.
In the dark forest the flowers are so pale
and the birds so shy.
Why is the wind full of whispered warnings
and the path dark with dire foreboding?
The sick god is lying in the shadow
and dreaming poisonous dreams.

Skogssjön

Forest Lake

I stood alone upon a sunkissed strand
beside the forest's pale blue lake,
a solitary cloud up in the sky
and on the water a single isle.
Ripe summer's sweetness pearled
from every tree
and into my opened heart
a single little drop ran down.

Höst

Autumn

The bare trees stand around your house
and slip endlessly into sky and air,
the bare trees climb down to the shore
and are mirrored in the water.
A child is still playing in the grey smoke of autumn
and a girl walking with flowers in her hand
and at the sky's rim
silver white birds fly up.

Nocturne

Ethereal silver moonlit evening,
night's blue billows,
waves glitter without number
follow one upon another.
Shadows fall over the road,
bushes on the bank weep softly,
black giants stand guard over the silver of the shore.
Silence deep in midst of summer,
sleep and dream –
The moon glides over the sea
white and tender.

Tidig gryning

Early Dawn

A few last stars are shining dimly.
I can see them through my window. The sky is wan,
you can barely sense the day beginning in the distance.
A silence lingers, spread over the lake,
a whisper lies in ambush among the trees,
my old garden is listening half distracted
to the breath of the night soughing over the path.

Det underliga havet

The Wondrous Sea

Strange fish glide through the deep,
unknown flowers shine on the bank;
I have seen red and gold and all other colours –
but the gaudy, gaudy sea is the most dangerous to look at;
it makes you thirsty and eager for the adventure about to
happen:
what happened in the story shall happen to me too!

Jag såg ett träd

I saw a tree

I saw a tree that was taller than all others
and heavy with cones hanging out of reach.
I saw a great church with open doors
and all the people coming out were pale and strong
and ready to die;
I saw a woman smiling through her make-up
wager her fate on a throw of the dice
and saw that she had lost.
A circle was drawn around these things
that no one may step over.

Nordisk vår

Nordic Spring

All my castles in the air have melted like snow,
all my dreams have flowed away like water,
all that remains of everything I loved
is a blue sky and a few pale stars.
The wind stirs gently among the trees.
Emptiness lingers. The water is silent.
The old fir tree stands wakeful, thinking
of the white cloud he kissed in a dream.

Hemkomst

Homecoming

The trees of my childhood stand jubilant around me, o men,
and the grass bids me welcome from a foreign land.
I lay my head on the grass: home at last.
Now I turn my back on everything that lies behind me:
my friends shall be forest, shore and lake.
Now I drink wisdom from the crown of the spruce moist
                                     with sap,
now I drink truth from the parched trunk of the birch,
now I drink power from the slightest most delicate grass
                                     blade:
a mighty protector mercifully stretches out his hand to me.

Min barndoms träd

The Trees of My Childhood

The trees of my childhood stand tall in the grass
and shake their heads: what has become of you?
Rows of columns stand like a reproach: you are unworthy to
come among us!
You are a child and ought to be capable of everything,
why are you imprisoned in the grip of sickness?
You have become a human being, strangely hateful.
When you were a child you held long conversations with us,
your look was wise.
Now we want to tell you the secret of your life:
the key to all mysteries lies in the grass in the raspberry bed.
We shall beat your brow, sleeper,
we shall wake you up, dead woman, from your dream.

Images

Poets Translated

Endre Ady 1877 – 1919

Ady Endre összes versei
Szépirodalmi Könyvkiadó
Budapest 1965

Gunnar Björling 1887 – 1960

Allt vill jag fatta i min hand
Ed. Erik Gamby
Fibs Lyrikklubb
Stockholm 1974

Vincenzo Cardarelli 1887 – 1959

Poesia Italiana del Novecento vol. 2
Ed. E. Sanguineti
Einaudi
Torino 1993

Rosalía de Castro 1837 – 1885

Obra Poética
Ed. Benito Varela Jácome
Bruguera
Barcelona 1975

Elmer Diktonius 1896 – 1961

Samlade dikter
Elmer Diktonius
Helsinki 1987

Vilhelm Ekelund 1880 – 1949

Svenk dikt
Ed. Lars Gustafsson
Wahlström och Widstrand
Stockholm 1982

Marie-Luise Kaschnitz 1901 – 1974

Deutsche Gedichte 1930 – 1960
Ed. Hans Bender
Philipp Reclam jun.
Stuttgart 1984

Klára Inotai 1922 – 1980

Private manuscript

Eeva-Liisa Manner 1921 – 1995

Kirkas, hämärä, kirkas: Kootut Runot
Ed. Tuula Hökkä
Helsinki: Tammi, 2008

László Marsall

Marsall László
Város papírmadárból
Cédrus
Budapest 1973

António Patrício 1878 – 1950

The Oxford Book of Portugese Verse
Ed. Aubrey F. G. Bell & B.Vidigal
Oxford 1972

Jan Skácel 1922 – 1989

Básně 1
Básně 11
Třebič
Czech Republic 2008

Edith Södergran 1892 – 1923

Samlade Dikter
Wahlström och Widstrand
Stockholm1987

Sándor Weöres 1913 – 1989

Weöres Sándor
Egybegyüjtött irások
Magveto Könyvkiadó
Budapest 1970
pp. 264, 265, 266, 271

Weöres Sándor
Áthallások
Szépirodalmi Könyvkiadó
Budapest 1976

Poesía de tipo tradicional

Antocogía de la Poesía Española
Lírica de tipo traditional
Ed. Dámaso Alonso y José Manuel Blecua
Gredos
Madrid 1978

J. Alberto Fernández Bañulus & Jose María Perez Orozco
Joyero de coplas flamencas
Biblioteca de la cultura Andaluza
Sevilla 1986

Antonio machado y Alvarez
Cantes flamencos
Colección Austral
Espasa-Calpe
Madrid 1975

The Spanish Traditional Lyric
Ed. J.G. Cummins
Pergamon
Oxford 1977

Translators

Erzsébet Csicsery-Rónay
Emily Jeremiah
Martina Jirankova-Limbrick
Hilary Kassman
Jim King
Simon Pettifar
Maria Schiller

Thanks for help to

Joseph Bebbington
N'tshuks Bonga
Warren Evans
James Fletcher
Alpo Kuparinen
Sidings
Philip Ward-Jackson